REDEEMING

THE TEARS

A Journey Through

GRIEF&LOSS

PICKINGUP
THEPIECES

ISBN: 1-5749-4186-0

Dewey Decimal Classification: 152.4
Subject Headings: GRIEF \ BEREAVEMENT \ SUFFERING

Unless otherwise indicated, all Scripture quotations are taken from the
Holman Christian Standard Bible®,
Copyright © 1999, 2000, 2002, 2003 by Holman Bible Publishers. Used by permission.

Scriptures marked NASB are taken from the *New American Standard Bible*®,
Copyright © 1960, 1962, 1963, 1968, 1971, 1972, 1973, 1975, 1977, 1995 by the
Lockman Foundation. Used by permission. (www.lockman.org)

Scriptures marked NIV are taken from the *Holy Bible, New International Version,* Copyright
© 1973, 1978, 1984 by International Bible Society. Used by permission.

To purchase additional copies of this resource or other studies:
ORDER ONLINE at www.SerendipityHouse.com;
WRITE Serendipity House, 117 10th Avenue North, Nashville, TN 37234
FAX (615) 277-8181
PHONE (800) 525-9563

1-800-525-9563
www.SerendipityHouse.com

Printed in the United States of America

11 10 09 08 07 06 05   1 2 3 4 5 6 7 8 9 10

CONTENTS

SESSION	TITLE	PAGE

GROUP DIRECTORY

Write your name on this page. Pass your books around and ask your group members to fill in their names and contact information in each other's books.

Your Name: _____

Name: _____	Name: _____
Address: _____	Address: _____
City: _____	City: _____
Zip Code: _____	Zip Code: _____
Home Phone: _____	Home Phone: _____
Mobile Phone: _____	Mobile Phone: _____
E-mail: _____	E-mail: _____
Name: _____	Name: _____
Address: _____	Address: _____
City: _____	City: _____
Zip Code: _____	Zip Code: _____
Home Phone: _____	Home Phone: _____
Mobile Phone: _____	Mobile Phone: _____
E-mail: _____	E-mail: _____
Name: _____	Name: _____
Address: _____	Address: _____
City: _____	City: _____
Zip Code: _____	Zip Code: _____
Home Phone: _____	Home Phone: _____
Mobile Phone: _____	Mobile Phone: _____
E-mail: _____	E-mail: _____
Name: _____	Name: _____
Address: _____	Address: _____
City: _____	City: _____
Zip Code: _____	Zip Code: _____
Home Phone: _____	Home Phone: _____
Mobile Phone: _____	Mobile Phone: _____
E-mail: _____	E-mail: _____
Name: _____	Name: _____
Address: _____	Address: _____
City: _____	City: _____
Zip Code: _____	Zip Code: _____
Home Phone: _____	Home Phone: _____
Mobile Phone: _____	Mobile Phone: _____
E-mail: _____	E-mail: _____

Redeeming the Tears: A Journey Through Grief & Loss

Excitement, happiness, adventure, love, laughter, freedom. beauty and hope ... these are words of life. From the beginning, we were created to live with passion and purpose. But when life is suddenly disrupted by the loss of someone or something important, everything changes. Like it or not, we all experience loss in our lives. Sometimes life is just flat out hard and our pain becomes almost unbearable.

Redeeming the Tears is designed to walk us through our grief, and with the support of those joining us on the journey, guide us to a hopeful place from which God can restore us to live out our lives in abundance, purpose, and hope. Healing occurs best in the context of community and relationships. We invite you to utilize this unique experiential resource as part of a small group or within a recovery ministry. God invites us to take the journey through our grief together so He can redeem our tears and help us to embrace hope and life again.

As we begin our journey through grief and loss, we're going to make use of an effective road map to deal with our grief. It's called finding a P.L.A.C.E. for the hurt. There are many different reasons for us to experience grief and loss just as there are many kinds of loss. Working through finding a P.L.A.C.E. for our hurt can help us understand where we are in the grieving process, as well as where we need to go to move toward healing.

Our Road Map
A P.L.A.C.E. FOR THE HURT

Position the event: What place does your loss have in your life's journey? Connect your memories of that moment and your emotions.

Listen to your heart: What does your heart tell you about yourself and the event?

Accept your Journey: What realities cannot be changed? Will you press on?

Connect with help: Will you reach out to God and other people for help?

Embrace Redemption: Are you ready to redeem your tears? Allow God to empower you to return to living life and to become a conduit for His healing work in others.

Welcome to Community!

Meeting together with a group of people to study God's Word and experience life together is an exciting adventure.

A small group is ... *a group of people unwilling to settle for anything less than redemptive community.*

Core Values

Community:
God is relational, so He created us to live in relationship with Him and each other. Authentic community involves sharing life together and connecting on many levels with the people in our group.

Group Process:
Developing authentic community requires a step-by-step process. It's a journey of sharing our stories with each other and learning together.

Stages of Development:
Every healthy group goes through various stages as it matures over a period of months or years. We begin with the birth of a new group, deepen our relationships in the growth and development stages, and ultimately multiply to form other new groups.

Interactive Bible Study:
God provided the Bible as an instruction manual of life. We need to deepen our understanding of God's Word. People learn and remember more as they wrestle with truth and learn from others. The process of Bible discovery and group interaction will enhance our growth.

Experiential Growth:

The goal of studying the Bible together is not merely a quest for knowledge, but should result in real life change. Beyond solely reading, studying, and dissecting the Bible, being a disciple of Christ involves reunifying knowledge with experience. We do this by bringing our questions to God, opening a dialogue with our hearts (instead of killing our desires), and utilizing other ways to listen to God speak to us (group interaction, nature, art, movies, circumstances, etc.). Experiential growth is always grounded in the Bible as God's primary means of revelation and our ultimate truth-source.

The Power of God:

Our processes and strategies will be ineffective unless we invite and embrace the presence and power of God. In order to experience community and growth, Jesus needs to be the centerpiece of our group experiences and the Holy Spirit must be at work.

Redemptive Community:

Healing occurs best within the context of community and relationships. A key aspect of our spiritual development and journey through grief and pain is seeing ourselves through the eyes of others, sharing our stories, and ultimately being set free from the secrets and lies we embrace that enslave our souls.

Mission:

God has invited us into a larger story with a great mission. It is a mission that involves setting captives free and healing the broken-hearted (Isaiah 61:1-2). However, we can only join in this mission to the degree that we've let Jesus bind up our wounds and set us free. As a group experiences true redemptive community, other people will be attracted to that group, and through that group to Jesus. We should be alert to inviting others while we maintain (and continue to fill) an "empty chair" in our meetings to remind us of others who need to encounter God and authentic Christian community.

Stages of Group Life

Each healthy small group will move through various stages as it matures. There is no prescribed time frame for moving through these stages because each group is unique.

Birth Stage: This is the time in which group members form relationships and begin to develop community.

Multiply Stage: The group begins the multiplication process. Members pray about their involvement in establishing new groups. The new groups begin the cycle again with the Birth Stage.

Growth Stage: Here the group members begin to care for one another as they learn what it means to apply what they have discovered through Bible study, shared experiences, worship, and prayer

Develop Stage: The Bible study and shared experiences deepen while the group members develop their gifts and skills. The group explores ways to invite neighbors, friends, and coworkers to meetings.

Subgrouping: If you have more than 12 people at a meeting, Serendipity House recommends dividing into smaller subgroups after the "Breaking the Ice" segment. Ask one person to be the leader of each subgroup, following the "Leader" directions for the session. The Group Leader should bring the subgroups back together for the closing. Subgrouping is also very useful when more openness and intimacy is required. The "Connecting" segment in each session is a great time to divide into smaller groups of 4 to 6 people.

Sharing Your Stories

The sessions in *Redeeming the Tears* are designed to help you share some of your personal lives with the people in your group as you learn to walk through your grief and embrace God's hope. Through your time together, each member of the group is encouraged to move from low risk, less personal sharing to higher risk communication. Real community will not develop apart from increasing intimacy of the group over time.

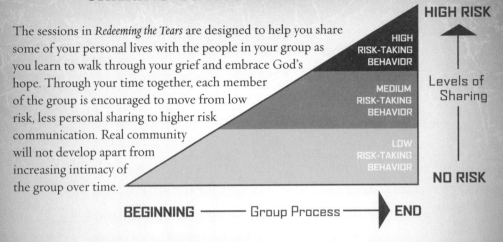

Sharing Your Lives

As you share your lives together during this time, it is important to recognize that it is God who has brought each person to this group, gifting the individuals to play a vital role in the group (1 Corinthians 12:1). Each of you was uniquely designed to contribute in your own unique way to building into the lives of the other people in your group. As you get to know one another better, consider the following four areas that will be unique for each person. These areas will help you get a "grip" how you can better support others and how they can support you.

G – SPIRITUAL GIFTS: God has given you unique spiritual gifts (1 Corinthians 12; Romans 12:3-8; Ephesians 4:1-16; etc.)

R – RESOURCES: You have resources that perhaps only you can share, including skill, abilities, possessions, money, and time (Acts 2:44-47; Ecclesiastes 4:9-12, etc.)

I – INDIVIDUAL EXPERIENCES: You have past experiences, both good and bad, that God can use to strengthen others (2 Corinthians 1:3-7; Romans 8:28, etc.)

P – PASSIONS: There are things that excite and motivate you. God has given you those desires and passions to use for His purposes (Psalm 37:4,23; Proverbs 3:5-6,13-18; etc.)

To better understand how a group should function and develop in these four areas, consider going through the Serendipity study entitled Great Beginnings.

Meeting Planner

The leader or facilitator of our group is _____.
The apprentice facilitator for this group is _____.

We will meet on the following dates and times:

	Date	Day	Time
Session 1	_____	_____	_____
Session 2	_____	_____	_____
Session 3	_____	_____	_____
Session 4	_____	_____	_____
Session 5	_____	_____	_____
Session 6	_____	_____	_____
Session 7	_____	_____	_____
Bonus	_____	_____	_____
Session 8	_____	_____	_____

We will meet at:

Session 1	_____
Session 2	_____
Session 3	_____
Session 4	_____
Session 5	_____
Session 6	_____
Session 7	_____
Bonus	_____
Session 8	_____

Refreshments will be arranged by:

Session 1	_____
Session 2	_____
Session 3	_____
Session 4	_____
Session 5	_____
Session 6	_____
Session 7	_____
Bonus	_____
Session 8	_____

Childcare will be arranged by:

Session 1	_____	Session 6	_____
Session 2	_____	Session 7	_____
Session 3	_____	Bonus	_____
Session 4	_____	Session 8	_____
Session 5	_____		

Group Meeting

Each of your group meetings will include a four-part agenda.

1. Breaking the Ice:

This section includes fun, uplifting questions to warm up the group and help group members get to know one another better, as they begin the journey of becoming a connected community. These questions prepare the group for meaningful discussion throughout the session.

2. Discovering the Truth:

The heart of each session is the interactive Bible study time. The goal is for the group to discover biblical truths through open, discovery questions that lead to further investigation. The emphasis in this section is two-fold: (1) to provide instruction about the grieving process; and (2) to understand what the Bible says through interaction within your group.

To help the group experience a greater sense of community, it is important for everybody to participate in the "Discovering the Truth" and "Embracing the Truth" discussions. Even though people in a group have differing levels of biblical knowledge, it is vital that group members encourage each other share what they are observing, thinking, and feeling about the Bible passages.

3. Embracing the Truth:

All study should direct group members to action and life change. This section continues the Bible study time, but with an emphasis on leading group members toward integrating the truths they have discovered into their lives. The questions are very practical and application-focused.

4. Connecting:

One of the key goals of this study to lead group members to grow closer to one another as the group develops a sense of community. This section focuses on further application, as well as opportunities for encouraging, supporting, and praying for one another.

Taking it Home:

Between each session, there is some homework for group members. This includes a question to take to God and a question to take to your heart, as well as a few questions to help you prepare for the next session. These experiences are a critical part of your grieving process.

Group Covenant

As you begin this study, it is important that your group covenant together, agreeing to live out important group values. Once these values are agreed upon, your group will be on its way to experiencing true Christian community. It's very important that your group discuss these values—preferably as you begin this study.

* PRIORITY: While we are in this group, we will give the group meetings priority. All the sessions are integrated, with each session building on the sessions that precede them. Committed attendance is vital to making your grieving process effective.

    NOTE: Due to the focus of this group on taking the journey through grief and loss, group sessions will require a full 90 minutes to complete, so plan accordingly.

* PARTICIPATION: Everyone is encouraged to participate, and no one dominates.

* HOMEWORK: The homework experiences are an integral and vital part of your grieving process. The assignments between each session include (1) A Question to Take to Your heart; (2) A Question to Take to God; and (3) A few questions to help you prepare for the next session.

* RESPECT: Everyone is given the right to his or her own opinions, and all questions are encouraged and respected.

* CONFIDENTIALITY: Anything that is said in our meetings is never repeated outside the meeting without permission for all of your group members. This is vital in creating the environment of trust and openness required to facilitate proper grieving and healing.

* LIFE CHANGE: We will regularly assess our progress as we move ahead in the grieving process. We will complete the "Taking it Home" activities to reinforce what we are learning and better integrate those lessons into our personal journeys.

* CARE AND SUPPORT: Permission is given to call upon each other at any time, especially in times of crisis. The group will provide care for every member.

* ACCOUNTABILITY: We agree to let the members of our group hold us accountable to commitments we make in whatever loving ways we decide upon. Unsolicited advice giving is not permitted.

I agree to all of the above_____ date: _____

BEGINNING THE JOURNEY TOGETHER

Everyone has grieved, is grieving, or will grieve at some point in their lives. Recognizing that loss and suffering are universal doesn't lessen our pain, but it can help create a common place where we all can find true healing. God is ready and able to sooth our hurts, calm our fears, and give us hope. *Redeeming the Tears* will walk us through our grief, and with the support of those joining us on the journey, guide us to a hopeful place from which God can restore our lives. Healing occurs best within a caring community.

In this session we will identify how people work through feelings of loss and discover that even though the pain is unique, we do not have to struggle alone.

OBJECTIVES FOR THIS SESSION:

- Discover how people tend to work through their feelings
- Recognize that grieving is normal and is vital to the healing process
- Begin to connect as a group and begin to share our stories with each other
- Introduce an effective way to work through grief called P.L.A.C.E.
- Set the stage for participation and freedom within the group using a Group Covenant

BREAKING THE ICE - 15 MINUTES

LEADER: *Be sure to read the introductory material in the front of this book and the Leader's material at the end of the book before the first session. Encourage everyone to answer the "Breaking the Ice" questions. After the two icebreakers, help your group members get to know one another by initiating introductions. You should introduce yourself first.*

1. Which of the following vehicles best describes your personality and why?
   - ❑ Mini-van – Practical and functional
   - ☑ Luxury sedan – I like my comforts
   - ❑ Sports car – Fast and furious
   - ❑ Compact car – Not much for style, but high in value
   - ❑ Off-road 4x4 – Go anywhere; try anything
   - ❑ Convertible – Enjoying the ride
   - ❑ Other: _____

Enjoy being alone but have enough space to grow

2. In the past year, what have you seen or experienced that made you laugh the hardest and why?

3. Take turns introducing yourselves to the group. Share your name, one thing about you that your friends would say is unusual or unique, and one reason you joined this group.

4. Before we continue, turn to the last page inside the back cover of your book. Review the "How ya' doin' really?" scale. Put today's date next to Week 1 along with the rating that best describes your emotional state right now.

OPENING PRAYER

God, it is no accident that each person has joined us for our time together. You have a purpose in each one being here. Please walk with us in our journey toward healing and give us a sense of commonality and comfort with each other as we participate in this group.

DISCOVERING THE TRUTH - 35 MINUTES

> LEADER: *Explain that in each session there is a "Discovering the Truth" section that provides understanding of the grieving process and opportunities to discover what the Bible says on the topic of the week. Be sure to leave 20 minutes for the "Connecting" time at the end of your group session. Read the explanations between the questions for the group.*

Life is about living with passion and purpose, but when that living is disrupted by the loss of someone or something important, we are bound to feel an emotional letdown and some degree of distress. Today we call this emotional letdown "grief." We have all experienced losses in our lives, and most of us have experienced a significant loss at one time. The intensity and length of the grief will vary from person to person, but the feeling of loss is still valid. Grieving is a process because there is a specific event that is at the beginning of our grief, and the feelings last well past the event. You may very well be in the midst of grieving over a loss or know someone who is. These next several sessions will help provide you with skills to walk through your grief.

1. Just as each person's grief is unique, the way each handles that grief will vary as well. Which of the following best describes you? When I am under stress, I will most likely:
   ❑ Bury myself in frantic activity
   ❑ Talk with the people around me
   ❑ Take time to be alone and reflect
   ❑ Other: _____

DOERS

Doers tend to find relief and comfort in activity. They release emotions by becoming involved in solving problems or fixing situations. For the doer, change may be accepted as a challenge. Yet when things, such as peoples' emotions, are uncontrollable, they may be very uncomfortable. Their emotions feel resolved in activity, movement, and busyness.

2. Think of person you know who is a total doer. What are the advantages of being a doer? On the flip side, what behaviors or attitudes might keep a doer from facing his or her pain?

FEELERS

Feelers seek out the closeness and warmth of other people. They draw strength from feeling that they are not alone. They may want to talk their feelings out. More emotional people may get the hurt out by explosions and outbursts. This often makes them well-balanced because they do not hold the pain in. Yet, they may never seem to get to closure because their emotions can easily take over.

3. How might a feeler best express his or her emotions? What advantages does this tendency have? What do feelers tend to do for the people around them? How might the way they relate to other people complicate their own grieving?

THINKERS

Thinkers usually want to take their time and process feelings. They may need to be alone. This can become very uncomfortable for the people around them who believe they need to be doing or talking. It may be especially hard for a thinker to open up and talk about their feelings. Sometimes thinkers best express their grief in art, poetry, or journaling.

4. Describe a thinker you know who has expressed his or her pain in some kind of artistic outlet? What are the advantages of the thinker's approach? Conversely, why would a thinker have a hard time being around people when grieving? Since they process best in solitude, what can we do to help thinkers in their grief?

Grief is a very stressful time in our lives. We have discussed three common ways to handle the stress related to grief. God has designed us with each of these tendencies, but one will rise to the top under stressful situations like grief. Regardless which of these tendencies describe you, it is important to accept that there is no one best way to deal with your grief. We hope that you will discover how to use your particular style through this process and benefit from sharing what you learn and experience with this group.

Asaph's Approach to Grief

Many of the psalms in the Bible are full of thankfulness and rejoicing in God's goodness, but there are many with a different flavor. Like everyone else on the planet, Asaph, the writer of some great psalms, grieved. Let's look at how he handled his grief.

LEADER: *Ask various members to read Bible passages when they appear during the session. Encourage individuals to respond to the questions as they feel comfortable. Some members may want to speak up while others may wish to remain quiet on certain questions. Strive for participation across the group rather than allowing one or two to carry the discussion.*

¹ I cry aloud to God, aloud to God, and He will hear me.
² In my day of trouble I sought the Lord. My hands were lifted up all night long; I refused to be comforted.
³ I think of God; I groan; I meditate; my spirit becomes weak.
⁴ You have kept me from closing my eyes; I am troubled and cannot speak.
⁵ I consider days of old, years long past.
⁶ At night I remember my music; I meditate in my heart, and my spirit ponders.
⁷ "Will the Lord reject forever and never again show favor?
⁸ Has His faithful love ceased forever? Is [His] promise at an end for all generations?
⁹ Has God forgotten to be gracious? Has He in anger withheld His compassion?"
¹⁰ So I say, "It is my sorrow that the right hand of the Most High has changed."

PSALM 77:1-10

5. How do you think Asaph is feeling about himself right now? About life? About God? Is this reaction normal following a loss or difficult time? Please explain.

6. What is Asaph's tone and attitude as he talked with God in the midst of his pain? What important step(s) do you see him taking as he approaches the journey through grief, loss, and pain?

7. Read over Psalm 77:1-10 again and take a couple of minutes to write down some words or phrases that describe your personal experience. What experiences, emotions, or questions about God and life caused words or phrases to jump out at you.

JESUS' APPROACH TO GRIEF AND PAIN

⁴ Yet He Himself [referring to Jesus] bore our sicknesses, and He carried our pains; but we in turn regarded Him stricken, struck down by God, and afflicted. ⁵ But He was pierced because of our transgressions [violations of God's law], crushed because of our iniquities; punishment for our peace was on Him, and we are healed by His wounds.

ISAIAH 53:4-5

¹ Let us ... run with endurance the race that lies before us, ² keeping our eyes on Jesus, the source and perfecter of our faith, who for the joy that lay before Him endured a cross and despised the shame, and has sat down at the right hand of God's throne. ³ For consider Him who endured such hostility from sinners against Himself, so that you won't grow weary and lose heart.

HEBREWS 12:1-3

8. According to these descriptions, what suffering did Jesus have to live through? What is the key lesson we can learn from Jesus' example in Hebrews 12?

9. At the end of Jesus' struggles, what were the benefits gained for Himself (Hebrews 12)? What were the benefits for others—in this case for us (Isaiah 53)?

EMBRACING THE TRUTH - 20 MINUTES

LEADER: *"Embracing the Truth" is the section where the group members will begin to integrate the truth they are discovering during the session into their personal lives. Be aware that the level of hurt and response to it will be different for different people, so the rate of life application will vary accordingly.*

As we begin our journey through grief and loss, we're going to learn an effective way to deal with that grief. It's called finding a P.L.A.C.E. for the hurt. There are many different reasons for us to experience grief and loss just as there are many kinds of loss. Working through finding a P.L.A.C.E. for our hurt can help us understand where we are in the grieving process, as well as where we need to go to move toward healing.

OUR ROAD MAP

A P.L.A.C.E. FOR THE HURT

POSITION THE EVENT: What place does your loss have in your life's journey? Connect your memories of that moment and your emotions.

LISTEN TO YOUR HEART: What does your heart tell you about yourself and the event?

ACCEPT YOUR JOURNEY: What realities cannot be changed? Will you press on?

CONNECT WITH HELP: Will you reach out to God and other people for help?

EMBRACE REDEMPTION: Are you ready to redeem your tears? Allow God to empower you to return to living life and to become a conduit for His healing work in others.

In the next session we'll "Position the Event" in the whole picture of our lives. This answers the question: "What place does my loss have in my life's journey? How will it affect me in the long run?" In this session, you have had the opportunity to share a little about your loss with the group and to better understand how you deal with things (as a doer, feeler, or thinker). The event or loss was a single point in time, but our pain is real and ongoing.

1. What are the key "pains" and losses in your life that bring you to this group?

Our challenged is to "run with endurance the race that lies before us"—to stay in our pain long enough to experience positive results on the other side of our journey. Remember Asaph, the guy who was so discouraged? Here's the rest of what he wrote in Psalm 77.

¹¹ I will remember the Lord's works; yes, I will remember Your ancient wonders. ¹² I will reflect on all You have done and meditate on Your actions. ¹³ God, Your way is holy. What god is great like God? ¹⁴ You are the God who works wonders; You revealed Your strength among the peoples. ¹⁵ With power You redeemed Your people, the descendants of Jacob and Joseph.

PSALM 77:11-15

2. What has changed in Asaph's attitude toward God? Why has his attitude changed? What does this psalm tell you about God's personality and nature?

God deeply desires to reach out to us and help us on our journeys. The Bible tells us that God is one, but that there are three persons—the Father, Son, and Holy Spirit. Let's see what the Holy Spirit does during our struggles.

²⁶ In the same way the Spirit also joins to help in our weakness, because we do not know what to pray for as we should, but the Spirit Himself intercedes for us with unspoken groanings. ²⁷ And He who searches the hearts knows the Spirit's mind-set, because He intercedes for the saints according to the will of God.

ROMANS 8:26-27

3. What does the Holy Spirit do for those who are in pain, feeling weak, and struggling? In what areas of life are you beginning to "grow weary and lose heart"? Where do you need to invite the Spirit's help?

4. Do any of the lessons we've learned give you added courage to keep running the race that lies before you even though it is difficult and painful? Which one(s)? If not, which of these areas do you struggle the most with?

- ❏ God is faithful and able to take you through your struggles, so have faith even if you feel abandoned
- ❏ If you stay in your pain, you will eventually experience the positive gains that God will bring to you and others.
- ❏ You are not alone. The Holy Spirit, God Himself, joins us in our struggles and helps us even when we don't know what to do or pray for.

CONNECTING - 20 MINUTES

LEADER: Use the "Connecting" time to help the group bond. The invitation during this session is for people to become comfortable opening up within the group. Encourage people to begin leaning on and supporting each other in prayer and in tangible ways.

LEADER INSTRUCTIONS FOR GROUP EXPERIENCE: See page 118 also.
Turn down the lights in the room, and use a menorah or a three-place candleholder to symbolize the presence of God. With the room dark or dim say, "Your life was going along normally when suddenly an event outside of your control struck and changed your life forever." Then, strike a match or ignite a disposal lighter. As you hold this small flame continue with, "In a moment, your life was dramatically changed. In that same moment though God—the Father, Son, and Holy Spirit—symbolized by this candle ... entered your life in a special way." Light the menorah or three candles. Feel free to briefly share about the darkness you experienced in your loss.

1. How abrupt was your loss? Do you feel as though this event of loss has changed your life forever? In what way, if at all, have you sensed God's presence during this time grief?

2. Review together the Group Covenant on page 12 of the book. Sign the covenant promising to begin the process of healing for yourself, as well as for those in your group.

3. We were designed to live in community, to help and support one another. What is one tangible thing this group could do for you this week? Write it down and then share it with the group.

4. If the Spirit is interceding "according to the will of God" for you, what do you believe the Holy Spirit is asking God to help you with right now as you experience and cope with your loss?
   ❏ That I might find Him in my grief
   ❏ That I would embrace and experience my pain so I can learn and benefit from it
   ❏ That I might become a more whole person as I go through this tough time
   ❏ That it eventually becomes a useful tool in His hands to help others
   ❏ That my understanding of pain makes me more like Jesus Christ
   ❏ Other: _____

5. Prayer is one key way we help each other by inviting God to work in someone's life. How can we pray for you today?

My Prayer Requests:

My Group's Prayer Requests:

In addition to praying for each other's specific needs, let's thank God that we're here together and that we've begun our journey. Let's ask Him for the courage to take this journey through our grief and loss together.

TAKING IT HOME

LEADER: *Explain that the "Taking it Home" section of each session will contain an introspective question to ask of your heart and a question to take to God. In addition, there is always personal activity to reinforce what the group has discussed. Strongly encourage everyone to complete the activities and questions before the next session. Be sure to highlight the importance of journaling memories or key insights that God reveals. These will greatly enhance both individual and group experiences in the grieving process.*

LOOKING INWARD ... A QUESTION TO TAKE TO MY HEART:

Look into your heart for the answer to the following question. This is introspection time—time to grapple with what drives your thinking and behavior, with what you believe in the deep recesses of your heart about God, yourself, and the world around you. Be sure to record your thoughts.

✳ As you identified yourself primarily as a doer, feeler, or thinker, ask yourself, "What about my way of processing my grief has been beneficial? What has been an obstacle? What obstacles must I overcome in order to keep working through my grief process?

LOOKING UPWARD ... A QUESTION TO TAKE TO GOD:

When you ask God a question, expect His Spirit to respond to your heart and spirit. However, don't manufacture an answer. Don't write down what you think the "right answer" is. Don't dig through the Bible looking for an official statement. Just pose the question to God and wait on Him. Be sure to record what you hear from Him.

Grief is a process that God created to help us deal with the inevitable losses of life. He intends the process to be for our benefit in the long run. Satan is real and working to stop us on our journey through grief and loss. To do this, he whispers lies to us that halt or slow down our progress.

✳ God, what lies have I been believing that have pulled me out of running the race that lies before me? What lies keep me from staying in my pain and taking the journey through my grief?

LOOKING FORWARD ... PREPARE FOR SESSION 2:

Please capture your thoughts and feelings on the following journal page as you work through your grief and healing process. Consider these questions that will be discussed in Session 2:

(1) What was your very first thought when you found out about or recognized your loss?

(2) What else had happened that day?

(3) Had anything similar to this ever happened to you before? Did you have any thoughts like, "I've been here before"?

(4) Are you aware of anything going on that helped prepare you for what was about to happen? Describe some of the ways God may have been preparing you beforehand.

Memories Journal

Positioning the Loss in My Life

In Session 1 we began our journey together through grief. We discussed that grieving is normal, even necessary, and we began to process our feelings. We also discovered that we are not alone and that God through His Holy Spirit wants to bring emotional and spiritual healing. In this session we will begin to use the road map introduced last time to position the event or loss in our lives.

A friend bought a gallon of milk during his lunch hour to take home. When he got home he discovered he had left the milk in the break room refrigerator at the office. If you were to ask him if he owned a full gallon of milk, he could answer yes, but couldn't give you a drink, because he did not have access to it. By learning the P.L.A.C.E. road map you will own a tool through which God and your group members can help you find comfort and healing. To access this tool though, you need to take the step of being open to engaging the group and God's Spirit.

Objectives for this session:
- Accept that everyone's pain is valid
- Identify emotions that are uniquely tied to grief
- Recognize how we prepare for and respond to loss
- Place our loss in context of our lives and connect it with our emotions
- Begin to recognize God's involvement even if we feel abandoned

---

Breaking the Ice - 10 minutes

LEADER: *The "Breaking the Ice" questions will help group members get better acquainted and begin talking casually about the session topic. Keep the tone of the conversation light and be sure everyone gets a turn.*

1. Share an embarrassing moment you had in high school or college. How did that moment affect you then? Does it affect you now? If so how?

2. Which of the film moments below best describes the current season of your life?
- ❐ When the angel gets his wings in the film *It's A Wonderful Life* – I love it when some one moves beyond who they were to what they had hoped to become.
- ❐ When the great white shark Jaws blows up in the first *Jaws* film – I'm very uncom fortable when danger is lurking in my comfort zone.
- ❐ When Dorothy wakes up in the movie *The Wizard of Oz* and realizes she has been dreaming – I need to feel at ease in my present reality.
- ❐ When Mel Gibson screams out "Freedom!" in the movie *Braveheart* – I want to over come the internal bondage of my present circumstance.
- ❐ When humans are released from the alien mother ship in the film *Close Encounters of the Third Kind* – I want to be reconnected to old friends.
- ❐ Other: _____.

3. What do you remember as your favorite toy when you were a child? How would you have felt if you had lost that toy?

Opening Prayer

Holy Spirit, please join us in our session today. We want to accept that our pain is normal, and okay. We appreciate the freedom to grieve in our own ways. Help us to be honest with ourselves, with each other, and with You. Strengthen each of us as we remember the event of our loss and begin to connect it to our emotions.

Our Road Map - 15 minutes

A P.L.A.C.E. FOR THE HURT

► **Position the event:** What place does your loss have in your life's journey? Connect your memories of that moment and your emotions.

Listen to your heart: What does your heart tell you about yourself and the event?

Accept your journey: What realities cannot be changed? Will you press on?

Connect with help: Will you reach out to God and other people for help?

Embrace redemption: Are you ready to redeem your tears? Allow God to empower you to return to living life and to become a conduit for His healing work in others.

In the first session we talked about finding a P.L.A.C.E. for our hurt. We acknowledged that grieving is normal and necessary. We also identified the various ways people tend to process life-changing events, and emphasized that the process of grieving is vital. Grieving was created by God to bring healing and strength to our lives after a loss.

1. How did your "Taking it Home" assignments go? Would you share a key insight that you gained from the question you took to your heart or the question you asked of God this week?

Your other homework was to ponder the following questions:
(1) What was your very first thought when you found out about or recognized your loss?
(2) What else had happened that day?
(3) Had anything similar to this ever happened to you before? Did you have any thoughts like, "I've been here before"?
(4) Are you aware of anything that was going on that helped prepare you for what was about to happen? Describe some of the ways God may have been preparing you beforehand.

2. What emotions or thoughts are you wrestling with after pondering these homework questions?

3. Last week we used a candle to illustrate how our lives can be dramatically changed in an instant. Each of you used the scale in the back of your book to capture how you were feeling initially. Again, let's turn to your "How ya' doin' really?" page inside the back cover of your book. Put today's date next to Week 2 along with the rating that best describes your emotional state right now.

DISCOVERING THE TRUTH - 35 MINUTES

POSITIONING THE EVENT

This week we're going to focus on understanding the "P"—how to position the event. We'll recount the moment we received the news or realized our loss, recall the events leading up to this moment, and try to connect our emotions with the memory. This is a necessary step if we're going to deal well with our losses. It's like watching a DVD movie or videotape. When we hold the remote, we're able to fast-forward and rewind the scenes of the story. This allows us to see the scene in the context of the *larger story*.

In most stories, there is a climactic event or a moment of impact. We can take our remote out and fast-forward or rewind to get to the main event in the story. In that frame, we will find a lot of emotion, thoughts, and beliefs. If we miss that moment, we will not understand the point of the whole story.

In your story, there is a moment of impact. There's a key point of hurt or pain or loss. In that frame of your life are many emotions that need to be expressed. NOTE: No matter how large or small your loss is, there are real emotions and valid pain to work through. There is always somebody with a greater loss than yours; that's not the issue. Every loss is important in your life story and the journey through your grief is vitally important to that story. To emotionally connect with your moment of impact, you need to go back and remember when you first heard about or experienced your loss.

1. What is your most vivid memory just prior to hearing about or realizing your loss? How were you feeling about life at this point before that loss or tragic event?

2. What was the first thing you thought or felt when you found out what happened?

Some Emotions That Can Accompany Loss

The Bible is full of references to God as an emotional being. Emotions, both enjoyable and painful, are given to us by God to enhance our experience of life and aid us in dealing with issues. The way we deal with loss is significant to our emotional, spiritual, and mental health. Let's look at some emotions that are unique to people during times of loss and grief.

* Feeling Disoriented (Confused): "I can't get this, I'm just numb.""
It's not unusual for a person to be confused when they receive news that is too big to handle. The body's reaction to confusion is disorientation. Accept this as very normal.

* Feeling Shock and Disbelief: "I can't believe this is happening!"
Many people make the move from confusion to disbelief. This can be like pulling down a wall. Once the facts settle in, we accept our situation and begin to pull the wall down ... sometimes brick by brick. Disbelief may also be our mind's way of saying, "This is just too big for me to handle, so I won't believe it is happening." This too is very normal.

* Feeling Disillusioned: "Why would this happen to me?"
Questioning "why" a tragedy or loss would happen can be part of the healing process. Many people ask God the "why" questions, and it's pretty common for people to blame God for what happened. Once again ... normal.

* Feeling Ambivalent: "I have divided thought and feelings"
Mental or emotional confusion results when our thoughts and feelings are divided. A person cannot accept two opposing thoughts at the same time. During the experience of loss, a person's emotions may confuse the facts with disbelief and doubt (e.g. we might intellectually know that God cares for us but ask, "If God really loves me, why did He let this happen to me?"). Initial ambivalence is normal.

* Feeling Angry: "I'm ticked off and don't want to understand."
There are certain emotions that surface during grief that are not usually there. Anger is like that. Suddenly we may find ourselves wanting to lash out at ourselves, others, or even the person who has left us. If people try to offer solutions or make us examine why we're angry, this can be even more frustrating! You guessed it ... normal.

3. What do the various emotions that accompany loss or grief seem to have in common? What do you think will happen if a person gets stuck in these emotions?

KING DAVID PLEADS FOR HIS SON

Throughout history people have experienced loss. It doesn't necessarily bring comfort to know that others have been where we are, but we can learn from those who have lived this unpredictable experience before us.

King David, who the Bible calls "a man after God's own heart," was forced to grieve. David was facing the very real prospect of the death of his infant son. Let's learn from his grief journey.

In David's culture, to fast and lie on the ground was a physical representation of someone's pleading spirit. As we saw before, and you may have experienced, a loss of appetite is not unusual during severe grief. This is far more than that. David is pleading for God's attention. He believes God can help so David tries everything in his power to prevent the inevitable.

Read aloud this story about King David:

16 David pleaded with God for the child. He fasted and went into his house and spent the nights lying on the ground. 17 The elders of his household stood beside him to get him up from the ground, but he refused, and he would not eat any food with them.

18 On the seventh day the child died. David's servants were afraid to tell him that the child was dead, for they thought, "While the child was still living, we spoke to David but he would not listen to us. How can we tell him the child is dead? He may do something desperate."

19 David noticed that his servants were whispering among themselves and he realized the child was dead. "Is the child dead?" he asked.

"Yes," they replied, "he is dead."

20 Then David got up from the ground. After he had washed, put on lotions and changed his clothes, he went into the house of the Lord and worshiped. Then he went to his own house, and at his request they served him food, and he ate.

21 His servants asked him, "Why are you acting this way? While the child was alive, you fasted and wept, but now that the child is dead, you get up and eat!"

22 He answered, "While the child was still alive, I fasted and wept. I thought, 'Who knows? The Lord may be gracious to me and let the child live.' 23 But now that he is dead, why should I fast? Can I bring him back again? I will go to him, but he will not return to me."

2 SAMUEL 12:16-23

4. What did David do hoping God would save his son (verses 16-17)? Did you do anything when faced with your impending loss? Please elaborate.

5. Do you think there was anything more David could have done to save his son? If so, what?

6. David prepared for his loss in two ways: (a) He started grieving in advance and (b) He ran to God. What is your opinion of David's approach? Did you have the opportunity to prepare emotionally for your loss? If so, how?

7. What did David do after he realized God had not spared his son (verse 20)? He seems to be nonchalant in these moments. Do you think that was the real emotion he was feeling? What emotions do you think were churning inside him?

EMBRACING THE TRUTH - 20 MINUTES

1. David pleaded with God for his son. What was your biggest request as you called out to God before and after the moment of your loss? How do you feel about the idea of pleading with God?

2. How would you describe your reaction the moment of your loss?

3. As you've relived the events surrounding your loss, is there anything you told yourself you wish you would have done? Please explain.

4. There are a variety of ways people cope with grief and prepare for loss. David's way was to grieve in advance. Which of the following best describes how you tend to cope?
   ❏ I stay busy to avoid thinking about the loss.
   ❏ I try to control the situations I am in.
   ❏ I isolate myself.
   ❏ I tell others and invite them into my loss.
   ❏ I've chosen to ignore this ever happened.
   ❏ I access and freely express anger.
   ❏ Other: _____.

5. In Psalm 51:6 (NASB) this same King David writes that God desires *"truth in the innermost being."* What might the way you cope with loss reveal to you about what you really believe about God, yourself, or perhaps the world in which you live?

6. This was one of the most devastating days of David's life, yet there is a redemptive quality to his words in verses 22 and 23. Even though it may be early in his grieving process, is there anything David said that may help you position your pain and perhaps begin to find some sense of understanding and comfort?

CONNECTING - 15 MINUTES

LEADER: Use this "Connecting" time to develop more closeness within your group, as well as to encourage and support one another in practical ways throughout the week. Invite everyone to join in and to be open and supportive with each other.

As we begin to position our losses, we have established that grieving is normal and is a process created for us by God that's vital for us to walk through if we're going to experience healing. Earlier in our session we discussed how the concept of positioning the event of loss in our lives is like watching a DVD movie or videotape. Let's try something.

LEADER INSTRUCTIONS FOR GROUP EXPERIENCE: See page 118 also.
Choose a movie to put in the DVD player or VCR that you set up before the session. Hit the Fast-Forward button and hand the remote control to one of your group members. Ask him or her to let it run a bit, and then randomly hit the Play button. Let the movie run for about 30 seconds and then stop it. Be sure people that have not seen this movie respond first. Then allow anyone who has seen it to fill in the blanks.

---

1. As you watched this random moment in the movie, were you able to understand why this moment was included in the movie? What is its significance in the overall story?

2. Sometimes our understanding of losses feels as random and confusing as watching a movie clip that we've never seen before out of context. What would help you to understand this short scene in the movie better? What would help you to better understand and position your loss in the larger story of your life?

3. At this point in your grief process, where are you with regard to positioning (remembering and connecting to emotions) the moment of your loss?

1	2	3	4	5	6	7	8	9	10
God being part of my loss is absurd to me			It's foggy but I can see the road signs				I have no problem understanding how God could let this happen		

4. How can this group support you practically and specifically this week in positioning your loss (placing your loss in the context of your life; understanding how you tend to cope and why; connecting your emotions with your memories; beginning to recognize God's involvement)? How can we pray for you today?

MY PRAYER REQUESTS:

MY GROUP'S PRAYER REQUESTS:

In addition to specific prayer requests, pray together for each person individually, that they would begin to let their memories and emotions begin to connect.

TAKING IT HOME

LOOKING INWARD ... A QUESTION TO TAKE TO MY HEART:

Look into your heart for what beliefs about God, yourself, and the world around you are driving your attitudes and behavior.

If you rated yourself below a "5" on question 3 above, ask your heart:

✶ "What do I think may be preventing me from facing loss or embracing my grief and walking/staying in it?" Once you have identified an obstacle, go to the Lord in prayer and, in your mind, drop and leave your obstacle at the feet of Jesus or lay it down at the cross!

If you rated yourself "5" or higher on question 3 above, ask your heart:

✳ "Am I rushing the process and perhaps pretending that things are fitting?
Do I need to let God help me position the event within the context of
the larger story?"

LOOKING UPWARD ... A QUESTION TO TAKE TO GOD:

Take this question to God this week and wait on His response. Don't try to anticipate
what He will say based on the Bible. Wait for Him to speak personally in a fresh way.

✳ "God, can you reveal obstacles that are preventing me from seeing where my loss fits in the larger story? Can you help me see why I
struggle to hook my emotions up with my memories?"

LOOKING FORWARD ... PREPARE FOR SESSION 3:

Please capture your thoughts and feelings on the following journal page as you work
through your grief and healing process. Consider these questions that will be discussed in
Session 3:

(1) What might be keeping me from facing my loss? Am I so overwhelmed in my pain
that I am becoming defined by my loss?

(2) What might be causing me to get stuck in my grief processing?

(3) Remember what we read in Session 1 about Jesus? "He Himself bore our sicknesses,
and He carried our pains" (Isaiah 53:4). Jesus has offered to take your pain and burdens and carry them for you. What emotions and burdens do I need to allow Jesus to
carry for me? How might handing over my burdens to Jesus help me?

(4) What pain might I need to embrace and be willing to wrestle with God about?

PERSPECTIVES JOURNAL

LISTENING TO MY HEART

In our last session we began to place the moment of our loss in perspective of our lives and the larger story. As we continue to open up to God and this group, listening to others' stories will become easier and more beneficial. Just as importantly, we will begin to listen to ours heart speak about the events or losses in our lives that are driving our grief. During this session, we will explore the importance of what we believe about our losses or painful events, about ourselves, about God, and about others. We'll focus on how our beliefs are powerful in directing our emotions, behaviors, and grieving process.

OBJECTIVES FOR THIS SESSION:
- Learn to listen to our hearts and be honest with ourselves about our beliefs and feelings
- Recognize that our deepest beliefs drive our emotions, behaviors, and healing process
- Grapple with the true and false beliefs that we have attached to our losses
- Understand the destructive power of embracing lies in the midst of our pain
- Accept the importance of wrestling with God over our questions and struggles

BREAKING THE ICE - 15 MINUTES

LEADER: The "Breaking the Ice" questions will help put people at ease and continue to help them connect with each other. The game "truth or lie?" in question 2 can be great fun, but it could consume a lot of time. Carefully monitor your time and stop when time is up. You can also ask people to minimize personal discussions during the game.

1. What was one of the longest nights of your life? What made it so long for you?
   - ❒ One of my first dates
   - ❒ Prom night
   - ❒ High school graduation
   - ❒ Waiting for the birth of my first child or giving birth to my first child
   - ❒ The night I passed a kidney stone
   - ❒ Waiting up for a child to arrive home
   - ❒ Wrestling with a major decision
   - ❒ Waiting for the antacid to kick in after too much pizza or Mexican food?
   - ❒ Other: _____

2. TRUTH OR LIE? GAME — Have each person tell one thing about themselves that is true and one thing that is false, without revealing which is which. Then have all participants try to guess which one is the truth. Take a vote by a show of hands each time.

OPENING PRAYER

God, let us begin to accept and embrace our emotions as they truly are right now. Help us to understand that what we really believe—about You, ourselves, others, and our sorrows—as a key to understanding and responding to our pain.

OUR ROAD MAP - 15 MINUTES

A P.L.A.C.E. FOR THE HURT

POSITION THE EVENT: What place does your loss have in your life's journey? Connect your memories of that moment and your emotions.

► LISTEN TO YOUR HEART: What does your heart tell you about yourself and the event?

ACCEPT YOUR JOURNEY: What realities cannot be changed? Will you press on?

CONNECT WITH HELP: Will you reach out to God and other people for help?

EMBRACE REDEMPTION: Are you ready to redeem your tears? Allow God to empower you to return to living life and to become a conduit for His healing work in others.

Each week we're talking about finding a P.L.A.C.E. for our hurt. As we worked to "position the event" in our last session, we rewound and fast-forwarded the tape of the event or moment of loss and reconnected our emotions with the event. We came to understand its influence on the whole of our life journey. We realized that the earliest thinking and conclusions following the moment of impact—losing a job, missing a great opportunity, losing a loved one, etc.—are very important in what we really belief about our loss.

1. How did your "Taking it Home" assignments go? Would you share a key insight that you gained from the question you took to your heart or the question you asked of God this week?

Your homework was to ponder the following questions:

(1) What might be keeping me from facing my loss? Am I so overwhelmed in my pain that I am becoming defined by my loss?

(2) What might be causing me to get stuck in my grief processing?

(3) Remember what we read in Session 1 about Jesus? "He Himself bore our sicknesses, and He carried our pains" (Isaiah 53:4). Jesus has offered to take your pain and burdens and carry them for you. What emotions and burdens do I need to allow Jesus to carry for me? How might handing over my burdens to Jesus help me?

(4) What pain might I need to embrace and be willing to wrestle with God about?

3. As you process your loss and the thoughts and feelings connected with it, what is your highest hurdle to overcome for your healing journey to continue?

4. Are there any thoughts, feelings, and struggles you feel you need to let Jesus carry? Please share these with the group. Which do you need to hang onto a while and continue to wrestle with God about them?

5. Again, let's turn to your "How ya' doin' really?" page inside the back cover of your book. Put today's date next to Week 3 along with the rating that best describes your emotional state right now.

DISCOVERING THE TRUTH - 30 MINUTES

LISTENING TO YOUR HEART

Last week we looked at range of emotional responses we experience during times of loss. In this session we're going to look into our hearts to begin to discover what beliefs are attach to our loss and pain. Our feelings and behaviors are a direct result of our beliefs—right or wrong. Because of this our emotions and behavior can reveal the deepest beliefs of our innermost being (Psalm 51:6 NASB).

This week we're going to focus on understanding the "L"—listening to your heart. This session is very important to the process since we will be listening to our hearts and finding out what internal agreements and vows we may have made because we have an enemy who doesn't sleep and stands ready to exploit our pain and our losses to his advantage.

Our journey toward healing will be greatly affected by these internal agreements and vows that we embrace about ourselves, our grief or loss, God, other people, and even the world in which we live. If we agree that something is true—whether it is or not—then we will certainly act upon that belief as if it were true. If we agree to a false belief or perception (what we are going to call a "lie"), then we will be focused in the wrong direction and delay or halt our progress toward healing.

INTERNAL AGREEMENTS WE OFTEN ACCEPT IN LOSS

There are set of beliefs that are very common to people experience loss or pain. Some or all of these beliefs likely describe your experience and issues you may be wrestling with. As we read each belief, let's keep in mind that struggling with these beliefs it not bad, but rather it is an important step for us. The problem comes in when we settle for embracing a lie and stop wrestling or engaging with God to discover what's really true. Here are internal agreements we may make to help us explain how we process our loss:

* *Abandonment or Betrayal: "I've been left all alone when I most need someone."*
We believe God has forsaken us in our deepest moment of need. He's turned His back on us when we needed Him most. We may also believe this about key people in our lives if they were not as available to us as we needed them to be .

1. If we embrace this belief, how are we likely to feel about God and relate to Him? Have you wrestled with feelings of abandonment and betrayal? Please describe your struggle.

* *Shame or Guilt: "I did something to deserve this." Or, "It's all my fault, if only I had ..."*
In an attempt to assess blame we turn on ourselves. If we made a mistake or were not prepared for the situation, we feel a sense of responsibility and true guilt. If we believe accidents and circumstances beyond our control are our fault, we experience false guilt. Remorse is the distress that arises from guilt. Shame is the sense of disgrace and unworthiness that follows..

2. If we embrace the lie that we are guilty for events outside of our control (false guilt), how are we likely to feel about ourselves in relation to God and others? What if we accept the lie that God could never forgive us for our true mistakes and failure?

* *Blame Others: "They are the villains in this story. If they could have just ..."*
If we don't blame ourselves, we may look for another imperfect human to blame ... a doctor who missed a diagnosis, a boss who acted unethically, and so on. Sometimes there is a person directly responsible for our loss. However, many times we are just driven by the lie that someone *has to be* responsible for our pain—someone *has to be* at fault.

3. Can anyone relate to this struggle? If so, please describe your experience. How might embracing the lie that someone always has to be at fault deter our healing journey?

* *Disillusionment with God: "I don't know what I believe anymore."*
During times of loss and grief, it's very common for people of faith to grapple with questions like, "How could a good or loving God allowing _____ to happen?" It is easy to call the goodness of God's heart for us into question or to embrace false ideas about God's concern, attention to detail, and the like.

4. Has disillusionment with God come into play in your journey so far? Please elaborate. How do you feel about the prospect of bringing these very honest thoughts and feelings to God to wrestle with Him?

* *Denial or Numbness: "I won't or don't feel anything."*
If we sense the situation is too big to cope with, we can easily shut down and become numb. Denial is an internal switch that God gives us enabling us to continue to exist until we are ready to engage. This switch normally resets over time. The trouble comes when we choose to stay numb. We reconnect when we go through the process of positioning our loss and choosing to wrestle with God to fit our loss into the larger story.

5. If we choose to live in denial, how might it affect how we relate to God or others?

LEADER: *The questions that follow will help people understand Jacob's story from the Bible. You may want to explain that the scene depicts a physical wrestling match, but the real battle is an emotional and spiritual one—a battle about our beliefs and questions. At times there are related personal application questions. However, most of the application questions appear in the "Embracing the Truth" section.*

WRESTLING WITH GOD

Many of us struggle with the concept of wrestling with God. And yet, most of us would like to pin Him down and hold Him until He provides us the answers we want and believe we deserve. There are questions we crave to get answered, such as: "How long the pain is going to last?" ... "Why has this happened in my life?" ..."Where were You God and where are You now?" ... "What do you expect me to do now?" ... "How can I move on with my life now that this has happened?" ... "How can a good Father let this happen to His child?" The good news is that God invites us to wrestle with Him. Wrestling with God is a critical part of our grieving process.

[24] *Jacob was left alone, and a man [God] wrestled with him until daybreak.* [25] *When the man saw that He could not defeat him, He struck Jacob's hip as they wrestled and dislocated his hip socket.* [26] *Then He said to Jacob, "Let Me go, for it is daybreak." But Jacob said, "I will not let You go unless You bless me."*

²⁷ "What is your name?" the man asked. "Jacob!" he replied.
²⁸ "Your name will no longer be Jacob," He said. "It will be Israel because you have struggled with God and with men and have prevailed."
²⁹ Then Jacob asked Him, "Please tell me Your name?" But He answered, "Why do you ask My name?" And He blessed him there.
³⁰ Jacob then named the place Peniel, "For," [he said,] "I have seen God face to face, and I have been delivered." ³¹ The sun shone on him as he passed by Penuel—limping on his hip.

GENESIS 32:24-31

6. According to verse 24, who was with Jacob when his wrestling match began? At what time of day do you think this bout started?

7. On a scale of 1 to 10 how alone do you feel in the late night hours?

1	2	3	4	5	6	7	8	9	10
Completely abandoned									Someone is always available to me

8. What was Jacob's motive for picking this fight? What was he seeking (verse 26)?

9. How long did Jacob wrestle with God even though he was in severe pain with a dislocated hip? Who do you think determined how long this bout would last?

10. What three "blessings" did Jacob walk away with after "prevailing" in his struggle (verses 28-29)? What would Jacob have missed if he had not persisted in his wrestling match with God? What would he have left with if he'd given up?

EMBRACING THE TRUTH - 15 MINUTES

1. We are not told what blessing Jacob wanted from God, but we know he walked away from the wrestling match satisfied with the three blessings God gave him. In your present situation, what do you want from God?

2. If God's goal was to defeat Jacob, He could have crushed him at any time. God let Jacob battle for an extended time until he was ready and able to receive the blessings God had for him. Who do you think will decide how long your journey through grief will last?

3. How long are you willing to wrestle with God in order gain peace of mind? What is it worth to you to receive the blessings God gave Jacob: a new name (fresh start and identity); reconnection and intimacy with God; "deliverance" from his pain? What might keep you from continuing to fight?

4. On the other side of this battle, Jacob walked away with two things: blessings and a limp. How do you believe God used both of these in his life?

CONNECTING - 15 MINUTES

Often in the moment we hear about or experience a loss, we adopt a belief or draw a conclusion that makes sense to us in the moment. As we've discussed, this belief could be right or wrong. Often that message is similar to something we have believed before.

As we are still and try listen to our hearts, we will often hear our "self talk" instead. These are the messages we lay over and over in our minds that keep us stuck in an emotional rut similar to the ruts in an old country road. As we continue to rehearse these thoughts, the ruts get deeper and deeper. Let's try a revealing group experience ...

LEADER INSTRUCTIONS FOR GROUP EXPERIENCE: See page 118 also.
Point out the bricks (one for each group member) you stacked up prior to this session. Ask your group members to close their eyes and imagine they are facing a brick wall. Explain that the wall represents those obstacles that stand in the way of moving beyond their pain and embracing life on the other side. Ask your group members to keep their eyes closed and ask God to reveal:

1. How tall and how broad is your wall?
2. When you face your wall, do you see an immovable mass, a long-term project, or a barrier easily removed?
3. Look around you. Is there anybody with you to help you tear down your wall?
4. Where is God in your picture? Next to you? Watching you struggle at a distance? On the other side of the wall? Nowhere in the picture?
5. How big is God in your picture?
6. In your picture, what does God want to do about your wall?
7. Are you ready at this point to take out the first brick from your wall? Everyone may not be ready and that's okay.

1. Let's discuss our exercise. What "self-talk" do you hear playing over and over in your mind?

2. Earlier, we discussed five beliefs that many people embrace: Abandonment/
   Betrayal; Shame/Guilt; Blame Others; Disillusionment with God; and Denial/Numb-
   ness. Is there one particular area in which you've been tempted to embrace a lie?
   Share your struggle with the group.

GROUP EXPERIENCE 2:

3. The first brick you remove from a wall is always the toughest one; the others fall more
   easily once the wall has been weakened. If you are truly ready to begin dismantling
   your wall, walk up one at a time, grab a brick, and discard it into the garbage can.

   Don't feel pressured to take this step today. This step will not move you any closer to
   the other side of the wall unless it is authentic. If you need more time, it's really okay.
   The bricks will be here every week until you are ready.

4. God is with us. We're all in this together. From this point on, we'll work side by side
   to tear down all of our walls. What are specific ways that we can pray for you and support you this week?

MY PRAYER REQUESTS:

MY GROUP'S PRAYER REQUESTS:

In addition to specific prayer requests, thank God for the journey you are on together
and pray for the courage to wrestle with God until you prevail over your loss.

TAKING IT HOME

LOOKING INWARD ... A QUESTION TO TAKE TO MY HEART:

Look into your heart for what beliefs about God, yourself, and the world around you are driving your attitudes and behavior.

✯ What are the nagging questions about my loss that I need to take to God? Why do these questions matter to me? What are the deeper questions that are really troubling my heart?

LOOKING UPWARD ... A QUESTION TO TAKE TO GOD:

Take this question to God this week and wait on His response. Don't try to anticipate what He will say based on the Bible. Wait for Him to speak personally in a fresh way.

✯ "God, were You there when my life got turned upside down? What were You doing at that time? How did You feel about what happened?

LOOKING FORWARD ... PREPARE FOR SESSION 4

Please capture your thoughts and feelings on the following journal page as you work through your grief and healing process. Consider these questions that will be discussed in Session 4:

(1) What lies have become attached to my loss or my hurt?
- ❏ Abandonment or Betrayal: "I've been left alone when I most need someone"
- ❏ Shame or Guilt: "I did something to deserve this." Or, "It's all my fault, if only I had ..."
- ❏ Blame Others: "They are the villains in this story. If they could have just ..."
- ❏ Disillusionment with God: "I don't know what I believe anymore."
- ❏ Denial/Numbness: "I won't or don't feel anything"
- ❏ Other: _____ .

(2) Are there other strong beliefs that I'm carrying around that could possibly be lies about myself, about God, or about my situation?

(3) 1 Peter 5:7 says that you should cast "all your care upon Him [God] because He cares for you." Do I really believe He cares for me and wants to carry my burdens?

(4) What cares and questions am I ready to hand over to God? What questions do I still need to hang on to and be willing to wrestle with God about?

Questions and Beliefs Journal

REALIGNING MY HEART

Hopefully the past week has been an intense but productive time of wrestling with God. Remember, we're all on this journey together, so let's continue to lift each other up. In our last session we discussed the importance of wrestling with what we believe about our losses or painful events, ourselves, God, and others. We discovered how powerful our beliefs are in directing our emotions, behaviors, and grieving process. During this session, we're going to take the next step in understanding the battle that is raging in our hearts and minds. To be successful as we continue to identify and expose the lies that get attached to our loss and pain, we need to align or realign our hearts with the larger story. If we want to tear down the brick wall that's blocking our path to life, joy, and peace, it's vital to see what's really going on.

A car that needs a wheel alignment will keep veering off the road. It's the same way with our hearts. When a loss or difficult event occurs, we hit a deep pothole and our hearts get misaligned. If we want to take a straight and steady journey through our grief, our hearts must be realigned—calibrated to the truth.

OBJECTIVES FOR THIS SESSION:
- Unveil the larger story and our part in it
- Disclose the unseen battle that is raging for our hearts, minds, and souls
- Discover some powerful spiritual weapons available to us
- Encounter God in the midst of our pain and struggles

BREAKING THE ICE - 10 MINUTES

LEADER: *Many of the people in your group may have experienced a tough week of wrestling with God or their hearts. The "Breaking the Ice" questions will help start the session on a lighter note and continue to help the group connect a little more. Try to keep the tone upbeat and fun. To be sure everyone gets a turn, encourage people to be brief.*

1. Where is your least favorite place to get stuck waiting and why?
   - ❏ Bumper-to-bumper traffic
   - ❏ The doctor's or dentist's office
   - ❏ The check-out line at the store
   - ❏ A hospital waiting room
   - ❏ The airport
   - ❏ An auto repair shop
   - ❏ Your least favorite relative's home
   - ❏ Other: _____

2. What is your favorite story from a movie or book (or one of your favorites)? Describe one or two elements of the story that make it a favorite.

OPENING PRAYER

God, we have all been wrestling with You and with our emotions. Many of us are just tired of being tired. Help us as we make our journey through the grief, to catch a glimpse of the blessings that await us beyond our walls and pain. Help us begin to grasp the larger story—the real story that we were born into and exist for.

OUR ROAD MAP - 15 MINUTES

A P.L.A.C.E. FOR THE HURT

POSITION THE EVENT: What place does your loss have in your life's journey? Connect your memories of that moment and your emotions.

▶ **LISTEN TO YOUR HEART:** What does your heart tell you about yourself and the event?

ACCEPT YOUR JOURNEY: What realities cannot be changed? Will you press on?

CONNECT WITH HELP: Will you reach out to God and other people for help?

EMBRACE REDEMPTION: Are you ready to redeem your tears? Allow God to empower you to return to living life and to become a conduit for His healing work in others.

As we walk through the process together of finding a P.L.A.C.E. for our hurt, we're going to build on our discussions from Session 3. As we began to "listen to our hearts," we started to recognize beliefs that have attached themselves to our loss or pain. Some of beliefs we have embraced are lies that have created a wall, blocking our path in life. We acknowledged that dismantling our walls is not quick and easy; it is truly a wrestling match with God and with our deepest beliefs.

1. How did your "Taking it Home" assignments go? Would you share any insight you gained into the deeper questions that are really troubling your heart? Others in the group will benefit from what you've experienced.

2. How about the question you asked of God this week? Did God tell you what He was doing or how He felt in the moment?

Your homework was to ponder the following questions:

(1) What lies have become attached to my loss or my hurt?
   ❏ Abandonment or Betrayal: "I've been left alone when I most need someone"
   ❏ Shame or Guilt: "I did something to deserve this." Or, "It's all my fault, if only I had ..."
   ❏ Blame Others: "They are the villains in this story. If they could have just ..."
   ❏ Disillusionment with God: "I don't know what I believe anymore."
   ❏ Denial/Numbness: "I won't or don't feel anything"
   ❏ Other: _____ .
(2) Are there other strong beliefs that I'm carrying around that could possibly be lies about myself, about God, or about my situation?
(3) 1 Peter 5:7 says that you should cast "all your care upon Him [God] because He cares for you." Do I really believe He cares for me and wants to carry my burdens?
(4) What cares and questions am I ready to hand over to God? What questions do I still need to hang on to and be willing to wrestle with God about?

3. Have you recognized any lies that you have embraced? Which one(s)?

4. Every one of us struggles at times with believing that God is good or that He really cares about our personal situations. How are you doing right now in believing that God cares about you and wants to carry your burdens?

5. Again, let's turn to your "How ya' doin' really?" page inside the back cover of your book. Put today's date next to Week 4 along with the rating that best describes your emotional state right now.

DISCOVERING THE TRUTH - 30 MINUTES

> *LEADER: In the initial part of "Discovering the Truth," you will begin to share with your group about the larger story we're a part of. Invite various members of your group to read the explanations and the Bible verses. Be sure to leave 15 minutes for the "Connecting" time at the end of your session.*

REALIGNING YOUR HEART

Remember, the first component of "L"—listening to your heart begins with accepting our emotions as they are right now. We then progress to wrestling with our hearts and with God to understand what we *truly* believe in our innermost being (Psalm 51:6) about our losses or hurts, about ourselves, about God, and about the world in which we live. Next, we ask God to reveal what lies we are embracing as truth. Be aware that God will speak to our hearts through various avenues: (1) Listening prayer; (2) Worship; (3) Nature; (4) Art, music, and film; (5) Books; (6) and of course Bible study!

The second component of "L"—listening to your heart is realigning our hearts by looking beyond our present situations and struggles to the larger story. With this perspective, we'll be able to continue the process of dismantling our walls.

THE LARGER STORY

We have discussed the need to understand our journey through grief and loss in the context of the larger story, but what does that really mean? This reference to the larger story goes beyond our journey through grief; it goes beyond our individual lives in this world; it even goes beyond the collective lives of humanity that span the centuries. The larger story began before there was life on earth. It's the story that we were all born into and exist for. Without it our lives are only a meaningless series of joyful and painful events followed by death. Here's the basic story:

THE GREAT BETRAYAL AND THE ORIGIN OF EVIL

Referring to Satan, the Devil:

[12] *Shining morning star, how you have fallen from the heavens! You destroyer of nations, you have been cut down to the ground.* [13] *You said to yourself: "I will ascend to the heavens; I will set up my throne above the stars of God. I will sit on the mount of the [gods'] assembly, in the remotest parts of the North.* [14] *I will ascend above the highest clouds; I will make myself like the Most High."* [15] *But you will be brought down to Sheol into the deepest regions of the Pit.*

ISAIAH 14:12-15

[14] *You were an anointed guardian cherub, for I had appointed you. You were on the holy mountain of God; you walked among the fiery stones.* [15] *From the day you were created you were blameless in your ways until wickedness was found in you.* [16] *Through the abundance of your trade, you were filled with violence, and you sinned. So I expelled you in disgrace from the mountain of God, and banished you, guardian cherub, from among the fiery stones.* [17] *Your heart became proud because of your beauty; For the sake of your splendor you corrupted your wisdom. So I threw you down to the earth; I made a spectacle of you before kings.*

EZEKIEL 28:14-17

THE GLORY OF MAN AND THE FALL INTO DARKNESS

[1] *In the beginning God created the heavens and the earth.* [27] *God created man in His own image, in the image of God He created him; male and female He created them.*

GENESIS 1:1,27 (NASB)

Referring to Satan, the Devil: [1] *Now the serpent was the most cunning of all the wild animals that the Lord God had made. He said to the woman, "Did God really say, 'You can't eat from any tree in the garden'?"* [13] *... "It was the serpent. He deceived me, and I ate."*

GENESIS 3:1,13

For all have sinned and fall short of the glory of God.

ROMANS 3:23

1. Because God wanted to be in relationship, He created humanity and paradise. According to verse 27, what was the original glory that God created in man and woman? Can you imagine ruling and reigning with God?

2. Does it surprise you God created free beings again after the fall and betrayal of Satan and one third of the angels with him?

3. Adam and Eve's disobedience and betrayal alienated us from our hearts and God. Who is the villain in this story and what was his primary tactic for ruining paradise, our intimacy with God, and our original glory into darkness (Genesis 3:1,13)? What was and is the villain's goal?

THE RESCUE MISSION

12 The Father ... has enabled you to share in the saints' inheritance in the light. 13 He has rescued us from the domain of darkness and transferred us into the kingdom of the Son He loves, 14 in whom we have redemption, the forgiveness of sins.

COLOSSIANS 1:12-14

We all, with unveiled faces, are reflecting the glory of the Lord and are being transformed into the same image from glory to glory; this is from the Lord who is the Spirit.

2 CORINTHIANS 3:18

4. Do you think God's original intent for us in Genesis has changed? According to Colossians 1, what has He done for us? What is His mission in our individual lives and for all of humanity?

THE UNSEEN REALITY

16 Therefore we do not give up; even though our outer person is being destroyed, our inner person is being renewed day by day. 17 For our momentary light affliction is producing for us an absolutely incomparable eternal weight of glory. 18 So we do not focus on what is seen, but on what is unseen; for what is seen is temporary, but what is unseen is eternal.

2 CORINTHIANS 4:16-18

Be sober! Be on the alert! Your adversary the Devil is prowling around like a roaring lion, looking for anyone he can devour.

1 PETER 5:8

5. What is the motivation for us to press on in our journey through grief and loss? What do we have to look forward to? How do the struggles we experience in this life compare to the unseen reality?

WHY BAD THINGS HAPPEN

(1) There is a villain in the story. (2) He uses lies and makes us question the goodness of God. (3) He uses live ammunition and his attacks are real. (4) His goal is to cause us to doubt the heart of God toward us. (5) God allows freedom, because without freedom of will, there is no love and relationship.

> LEADER: Share the following overview of a "Critical Path to Healing." Read the explanations in this section and don't worry if you don't have all the answers. Each person's journey and part in the larger story is unique. Only God has all the answers. Involve group members by asking for volunteers to read. Explain that it's only necessary to gain a general understanding now. Things will become clearer throughout the journey. Keep things moving forward.

A CRITICAL PATH TO HEALING

Once our hearts and minds are realigned to recognize the unseen reality and the battle that is being waged for our hearts and our souls, the pain and struggles in our own lives come into clearer focus. Colossians 1 says God "has rescued"—a past tense, completed work. Even though God has already sealed Satan's fate through the death and resurrection of Jesus Christ, Satan is still "prowling around" (1 Peter 5:8) and using his primary tactic of lying to take us out! He wants to make us believe that God is not good, to wreak pain and havoc in our lives, and ultimately to destroy us. Satan and his demonic forces want to keep us out of the glory that we were intended to live in, and the intimacy that God wants us to share with Him. With that in mind, let's look at a Critical Path to Healing, which displays common threads in each person's brokenness and recovery.

* *Strategic ARROWS are launched into our lives create WOUNDS*   ... A tragic loss.

* *Our WOUNDS become infected with LIES or false beliefs*   ... "God has abandoned you."

* *Satan continues to repeat LIES until we make AGREEMENTS to accept them as truth*
     ... "I'm on my own now."

* *Once AGREEMENTS are made VOWS are soon to follow* ... "I will always/never again ..."

* *False agreements and vows feed our FALSE SELF* ... Our distorted belief about who we are.

It's important to understand that this Critical Path to Healing is not necessarily linear. We all enter it at different points in different situations. The key to recovery is recognizing that we will likely have to battle in one or more of the following areas to experience God's healing and blessing:
• Identify and renounce the lies that we've embraced
• Break the agreements we've made with the lies and replace them with truth
• Denounce the vows we've made and replace old vows with new ones
• Refuse to live out of our false self and embrace who we really are in Christ

6. Do the Larger Story and Critical Path to Healing begin to shed any light on your situation? Can you see ways the enemy has exploited your wounds?

EMBRACING THE TRUTH ~ 20 MINUTES

If this is an unseen spiritual battle we're in, how do we fight it? How do we engage and prevail over our adversary individually and as a group that's in this battle together? What weapons can we use?

WEAPONS IN THE SPIRITUAL BATTLE

¹¹ Put on the full armor of God so that you can stand against the tactics of the Devil. ¹² For our battle is not against flesh and blood, but against the rulers, against the authorities, against the world powers of this darkness, against the spiritual forces of evil in the heavens. ¹³ This is why you must take up the full armor of God, so that you may be able to resist in the evil day, and having prepared everything, to take your stand. ¹⁴ Stand, therefore, with truth like a belt around your waist, righteousness like armor on your chest, ¹⁵ and your feet sandaled with readiness for the gospel of peace. ¹⁶ In every situation take the shield of faith, and with it you will be able to extinguish the flaming arrows of the evil one. ¹⁷ Take the helmet of salvation, and the sword of the Spirit, which is God's word. ¹⁸ With every prayer and request, pray at all times in the Spirit, and stay alert in this, with all perseverance and intercession for all the saints.

EPHESIANS 6:11-18

1. Who is identified in Ephesians 6:11-12 as the enemy in the battle for our hearts and minds? Who have you been battling with since your loss? Have you been diverted from battling the real enemy? If so, how?

2. In which of the following area(s) do you feel the strongest assaults coming at you? Which spiritual weapon or weapons do you need to take hold of to stand against the enemy's assaults? Will you plead with God to provide the protection you need?

❏ Instead of hiding and secrets, I want to experience the freedom to be myself, and the freedom to be real with God and with others.
   WEAPON: *Truth ... the reality of God's presence and direction in our innermost being (refer to Psalm 51:6) and acknowledgment that God is truly light and life*

❏ I want strength to guard my heart so that my pain doesn't lead me to embrace temptations that will drag me down into addictions and compulsive behaviors.
   WEAPON: *Righteousness ... living our lives according to what God reveals and directs us to do; upright character and loyalty to God's ways*

❏ As the enemy's arrows and lies bombard my mind and heart, I want to stand strong without wavering. I long for single-minded resolve and peace.
   WEAPON: *Knowledge of and dependence on the gospel ... fully realizing and embracing God's provision for forgiving and redeeming us through Jesus*

❏ The enemy's arrows are fiery, intense, and unrelenting in my life. I want to knock down the arrows and extinguish the fires of fear, doubt, selfishness, discouragement, and temptation.
   WEAPON: *Faith ... being firmly convinced that God is good and then placing complete trust in Him*

❏ Because of past wounds in my life and lies I have embraced, I am in bondage. Until I'm set free from the oppressive prison of my past and my pain, my mind is a ready target. I need protection for my mind ... and heart.
   WEAPON: *Salvation ... personal experience of Jesus, our salvation; our confidence of protection from the power of arrows and sin, as well as our strong assurance and hope of eternity with Him*

❏ As diverse messages keep swirling through my mind and my feelings bounce all over, I want to be sure that I'm clearly discerning what is a lie and what is the truth.
   WEAPON: *Sword of the Spirit ... God's word captured in the Bible and clarified and illuminated in our hearts by the Holy Spirit, "the Spirit of truth" who stays with and lives in every Christ-follower (John 14:17)*

❏ I get tired of the struggles and the pain. I know God is there, but I need other people that care and understand enough to walk with me and support me in the battles.
   WEAPON: *The Holy Spirit counts it such a privilege to come alongside us in our battles to help us regain our stride (John 14:16-17). In prayer for ourselves and each other, we continue to invite the awesome power of the Spirit into our struggles ... and give each other the support and encouragement we need.*

CONNECTING - 15 MINUTES

In our last session, we envisioned a brick wall as a representation of obstacles that stand in the way of moving beyond our pain and embracing life on the other side of it. For most, if not all of us, we see dismantling our walls as very difficult efforts. What we now realize is that there are vicious assaults on us, trying to prevent us from dismantling those walls (2 Corinthians 10:4-5) so that we will stay stuck or give up altogether. In this next group experience, we'll again listen to our hearts and to God.

1. Okay, let's discuss what we saw. What were the arrows? When were they launched into your life? What have the repeated messages been and how have you typically responded to them?

2. Look back in the "Embracing the Truth" section at the assaults and spiritual weapons that God provides for us. Are there specific weapons that you need to utilize more regularly? Elaborate on your battles.

3. Each person should take an arrow (or dart) from the pile as a needed reminder of the unseen battle and as an encouragement that as we draw near to God, we have access to powerful spiritual weapons when we are attacked again. What are specific ways that we can pray for you and support you this week?

MY PRAYER REQUESTS:

MY GROUP'S PRAYER REQUESTS:

In addition to specific prayer requests, thank God for the larger story and His presence and provision in the unseen battle. Pray for the courage to acknowledge our vulnerabilities and put on the full armor of God.

TAKING IT HOME

LOOKING INWARD ... A QUESTION TO TAKE TO MY HEART:

Look into your heart for what beliefs about God, yourself, and the world around you are driving your attitudes and behavior.

❋ "Are there past wounds infecting and intensifying my present loss?"
After you identify these past wounds, ask you heart: "What beliefs
were attached to the wounds and what vows have you taken (I will
always ... or I will never again ...)?"

LOOKING UPWARD ... A QUESTION TO TAKE TO GOD:

Take this question to God this week and wait on His response. Don't try to anticipate
what He will say based on the Bible. Wait for Him to speak personally in a fresh way.

❋ "God, how do feel about me? Do You actually enjoy me and my journey or do You just graciously put up with me?"

LOOKING FORWARD ... PREPARE FOR SESSION 5

Please capture your thoughts and feelings on the following journal page as you work
through your grief and healing process. Consider these questions that will be discussed in
Session 5:

(1) In my heart of hearts, what doubts do I sometimes have about God?
(2) How would I change my life and the situation I'm in now?
(3) What burdens have I been able to hand over to the Holy Spirit? Which ones have I
chosen to bear myself?
(4) I am willing to stop arranging my life? Why do I need to be in control? What's that
really all about?

ARROWS JOURNAL

Accepting My Journey

None of us chose the journey we're taking. No one chooses pain and loss. In fact, we'd jump ship right now if we thought it would help. When we were together the last time we discovered that our story (our pain and circumstances) only has meaning in the context of the larger story. We clearly recognized that Satan would like nothing more than for us to jump ship right into the waiting jaws of a shark. He wants to cut off our journey by making us believe God is not good, and by wreaking more pain and havoc in our lives. There are unseen forces that want to keep us out of the glory we are intended to live in and the intimacy God wants us to share with Him.

So, forced onto the boat traveling through grief and pain, we must choose to settle into the journey. If we jump ship we'll land in the murky waters of discontentment, bitterness, anger, or fear and then die in our pain. The only option is to settle in, do all we can, and trust God to guide our journey toward spiritual and emotional healing. While we're on board we're going to have to deal with some hard questions, including the "why?" questions.

Objectives for this Session:
- Accept that we are on a journey and that God loves us so much He's taking the journey with us
- Begin to accept the realities of our situations and the circumstances beyond our control
- Understand what's really behind all of our "why" questions
- Embrace the journey through our grief with hopeful anticipation of what God will do

Breaking the Ice - 10 minutes

LEADER: *Again, make these "Breaking the Ice" questions fun as you start the session. You'll learn more about each other's stories, especially in question 3. The goal as always is to give everyone a chance to participate in responding to the questions.*

1. Which song best describes how you responded when you asked your parents a question but they chose not to answer your question?
   ❏ Takin' Care of Business – "I demanded an answer."
   ❏ Achy Breaky Heart – "I pouted. It hurt my feelings."
   ❏ Let It Be – "I accepted it and went on about my business."
   ❏ Bridge Over Troubled Water – "After this happened a few times I decided they weren't going to answer, so in frustration I stopped asking."
   ❏ Other: _____ .

2. When you were a teenager, was there ever a time when you were forced to take (field trip, family vacation, etc.)? Where did you go? Why didn't you want to make the trip? What was your attitude while on the trip?

3. If you could ask God one question about your circumstances knowing He would give you an answer, what would that question be?

Opening Prayer

God, there are some things in life we will never understand. Frankly, this is usually hard to accept. Even though You invite us to bring our "whys" to You, tonight we want to ask You what You are doing in our journey rather than just ask "why?" Please speak to us. We need and long for answers.

Our Road Map - 15 minutes

A P.L.A.C.E. FOR THE HURT

Position the event:	What place does your loss have in your life's journey? Connect your memories of that moment and your emotions.
▶ Listen to your heart:	What does your heart tell you about yourself and the event?
Accept your journey:	What realities cannot be changed? Will you press on?
Connect with help:	Will you reach out to God and other people for help?
Embrace redemption:	Are you ready to redeem your tears? Allow God to empower you to return to living life and to become a conduit for His healing work in others.

With the perspective of the larger story and the unseen battle being waged in our lives, we began in the last session to "realign our hearts." We discovered that looking beyond our current circumstances and trusting God's love, His truth, and His power could make a world of difference in how we approach our grief and pain.

During this session we're going to take a big leap of faith. This may not be an easy leap, but it may be the most liberating. We're going to begin to "accept our journeys."

1. How did your "Taking it Home" assignments go? Would you share any insight you gained about past wounds? Did God tell you how He feels about you?

Your homework was to ponder the following questions:
(1) In my heart of hearts, what doubts do I sometimes have about God?
(2) How would I change my life and the situation I'm in now?
(3) What burdens have I been able to hand over to the Holy Spirit? Which ones have I chosen to bear myself?
(4) I am willing to stop arranging my life? Why do I need to be in control? What's that really all about?

2. We've discussed how important our beliefs are in driving our emotions and behaviors. We all have doubts at different points in our lives. Have you become aware of true heart beliefs about God that surprised you? Please explain.

3. What do you think it would take for you to commit to staying with your pain and allow God to control where He takes you from here?

4. Again, let's turn to your "How ya' doin' really?" page inside the back cover of your book. Put today's date next to Week 5 along with the rating that best describes your emotional state right now.

Discovering the Truth - 35 minutes

LEADER: *In the initial part of "Discovering the Truth," you will delve into the topic of "why" questions. To keep group members involved, invite various members of your group to read the explanations for why we ask "why" questions. After this topic, you'll examine the story of Joseph. Be sure to leave 15 minutes for "Connecting" at the end of your session.*

On our journey, we're going to struggle with fundamental questions about life, death, and what happens next. In those moments when troubling situations occur, we grasp for an answer to the question that has plagued us since Adam and Eve walked the earth: "Why?" God has made us with minds that want to find reason and meaning in whatever we do. Just pay attention to children watching clouds go by and listen to them discuss the amazing things they see. They ask the same questions we ask in many situations. Where did this come from? Who caused this? Why is it here? How does it affect my world? When things don't make sense to us, then we have difficulty accepting our situations and moving on. We want answers, but some of our answers will only be found in the "A" of "accepting our journey."

1. Why do you think we so often ask "why" questions?

Why? Why? Why?

People want answers to this question. Some receive an answer. They may like the response, or they may not. Many never receive the answers they're looking for. The problem is that too many times we simply ask the wrong question! Rather than asking, "Why did this happen?" or "Why did this happen to me?" ... a better question is, "God, what are you doing in me and through me in this circumstance? God, what are You up to and how are You going to redeem my life and through this painful situation?"

The truth is that if God gave us all the information that He knows about our circumstances, it would be way too much for us to handle. We would probably mess up the blessings He has planned for us. God is on our journey with us and He wants us to invite Him into our pain and loss, and then to trust Him to lead us through our grief.

2. If you were all-knowing and all-powerful like God, how would the world be different?
   ❏ I'd be certain the situation I'm dealing with never happens to anyone else.
   ❏ I'd never let anyone feel the pain I'm feeling.
   ❏ I'd be certain bad things never happened to good people.
   ❏ I'd make sure people live forever.
   ❏ Other: _____.

Why do you think God doesn't do the thing that you would do in His shoes?

WHY WE ASK "WHY" QUESTIONS

I Need Nurturing: "It's my turn to be cared for by others."
It's normal to want to express our pain and receive comfort. But when our desire to be cared for becomes a pattern of complaining and self-focus, then it's time to let go of the hurt and give it to God, get unstuck, and continue our journey through grief so we can get back into living again.

I Want Control: "If I lose control something bad may happen."
God doesn't hold us responsible for those things over which we have no control. Unfortunately, we tend to grab for control when we don't like how life is going. When we take responsibility for events outside of our control, we feel false guilt. When we have made a mistake, true guilt sets in. If we don't accept God's forgiveness and reject false guilt, we can get stuck in guilt and shame. When we release control and trust that God will come and redeem even the worst of events, we have taken a huge step toward being free of the bondage that accompanies grief.

I Need to Express My Anger: "Just let me express myself in the ways I need to."
Getting anger out is healthy and necessary. But releasing anger does not bring healing in and of itself; it is just a release. Therefore, there comes a time when you must put an end to the venting. If we allow ourselves to get stuck in venting, we will eventually become isolated and bitter. If we take our emotions to God, He will help us resolve them and give us hope.

I Have to Know: "I'll never rest until all my questions are answered."
Finding the answers to all of our questions is not going to happen. As long as we press to have all of our questions answered, we will allow ourselves to be enslaved to our circumstances. Our entire lives revolve around one single moment in time, keeping us in bondage. If we have faith that God is giving us all the information we need, as we need it, we are again free to allow healing to take place.

I Want Revenge: "I want someone else to pay—to hurt as much as I do."
It is not unusual to want God or others to hurt as deeply as we do. But a continued insistence on revenge stokes bitterness and leads to despair. Again, we place ourselves in bondage to a single event in our lives so that it controls and eventually consumes us. If thoughts of revenge last for long periods of time or we feel compelled to act on those thoughts, it is important to speak with a minister or Christian counselor. God promises to take care of justice and vengeance, and to free us from its bondage, if we will release our desire for revenge to Him.

LEADER: *Use these questions to help group members interact about the concepts just discussed. Encourage open and honest dialogue and be sure to focus on accepting people where they are and encouraging them to take another step with God in the journey.*

---

3. Describe a time in your life when you did something spontaneously that was fun and exhilarating—something that demanded you to take things one step at a time without knowing how the next step would be accomplished. How did it go? How did it make you feel?

4. How do you feel when a situation is completely out of your control?
   ❑ I feel I am a loser because I don't have the skills or power to control the situation.
   ❑ I feel anger because I was placed in this uncontrollable situation.
   ❑ I feel overwhelmed because I have already been forced to handle my present uncontrollable situation, and now I must deal with another.
   ❑ I feel on edge because I believe something bad is going to happen if I can't find some way to control this situation.
   ❑ I feel picked on. Why do uncontrollable situations continue to happen to me?
   ❑ Other:

5. Are there any common themes for why we ask "why" questions? Where do they all lead if we get stuck in them and choose not to release them?

A JOURNEY JOSEPH DIDN'T CHOOSE

Joseph was a great example of someone who could have been bitter and angry about his situation, but accepted the realities he could not change, and lived on. Let's look at his story.

Narrator:
[5] Then Joseph had a dream. When he told it to his brothers, they hated him even more. [6] He said to them,

Joseph (Reader 1):
"Listen to this dream I had:
[7] There we were, binding sheaves of grain in the field. Suddenly my sheaf stood up, and your sheaves gathered around it and bowed down to my sheaf."

All Males but Reader 1 Read:
[8] "Are you really going to reign over us? ... Are you really going to rule us?"

Narrator:
So they hated him even more because of his dream and what he had said.

GENESIS 37:5-8

Narrator:
Later ... [18] They saw him in the distance, and before he had reached them, they plotted to kill him. [19] They said to one another,

All Males but Reader 1 Read:
"Here comes that dreamer!
[20] Come on, let's kill him and throw him into one of the pits. We can say that a vicious animal ate him. Then we'll see what becomes of his dreams!"

GENESIS 37:18-22

His brothers did just as they had planned. Joseph was thrown into a deep pit, picked up by some strangers, and sold into slavery. Once a slave, God delivered him and he became prosperous. Later, he was betrayed and thrown back into slavery. In the dry and dusty heat, he labored. His rights were completely violated. He was stripped of his identity and he was destitute.

BITTER OR BETTER

Joseph eventually became second in command for all of the great kingdom of Egypt. His brothers—the same brothers who had thrown him into the pit—became destitute and came begging for his help. He brought his brothers into his home and explained to them that, even though they had intended evil for his life, God had redeemed his tears. Here's what happened between Joseph and his brothers.

Narrator:
¹⁹ But Joseph said to them,

Joseph (Reader 1):

"Don't be afraid. Am I in the place of God? ²⁰ You planned evil against me; God planned it for good to bring about the present result—the survival of many people. ²¹ Therefore don't be afraid. I will take care of you and your little ones."

Narrator:
And he comforted them and spoke kindly to them.

GENESIS 50:19-21

1. So, why did Joseph's brothers throw him in the pit? Do you think he deserved the treatment he received?

2. Which of questions below do you think might have been most prominent in Joseph's mind while going through his long season of captivity and turmoil? What has your most searching question been so far?
   ❏ Did I cause this?
   ❏ God, are You in my situation?
   ❏ Why would people (my brothers) do this to me?
   ❏ How can You possibly bring somethiing good from this?
   ❏ God, why would you allow this to happen to me?
   ❏ Could this have been prevented, God?
   ❏ Other: _____

3. From the time Joseph was taken into slavery, until the time he became governor of Egypt was 13 years. His journey was long and difficult. What realities do you think Joseph had to accept on his journey? What would've happened to Joseph if he had settled into the negative realities all around him?

4. What character traits did you see in Joseph as a young man—before he was thrown into the pit by his brothers?

5. What character traits did you see in Joseph when his brothers came to him for help years later? How could someone who lost so much become such an amazing leader?

6. What were the positive outcomes of Joseph's willingness to accept his journey and trust God to ultimately redeem it?

EMBRACING THE TRUTH - 15 MINUTES

LEADER: This section will help your group members begin to integrate the truths from Joseph's life into their own journeys.

1. Joseph's brothers told their dad that vicious animals had killed Joseph. Those lies caused Jacob to grieve his loss "for many days" (Genesis 37:34) because he embraced a lie and as true. Are any lies that Satan has been misleading you with, lies that are causing you to doubt the love of God?

2. Are you finding yourself settling into any of the following patterns that have prevented you from accepting your journey and staying in your pain? Please explain.
   - ❏ I Need Nurturing: "It's my turn to be cared for by others."
   - ❏ I Want Control: "If I lose control something bad may happen."
   - ❏ I Need to Express My Anger: "Just let me express myself in the ways I need to."
   - ❏ I Have to Know: "I'll never rest until all my questions are answered."
   - ❏ I Want Revenge: "I want someone else to pay—to hurt as much as I do."
   - ❏ Other:

3. What realities do you believe you'll need to accept on your journey? What do you think might happen to you if you embrace the dark realities of your present situation?

At the end of his life, Joseph looked back and saw that many people had benefited because of his suffering and willingness to accept his journey (Genesis 50:15-21). Because he had been sent into Egypt, he was in exactly the right place to prepare for the famine. He would not have been there if his brothers had not done evil toward him. God actually used their wicked deed and Joseph's suffering to bring about a greater good. Joseph accepted his situation and did the best he could do throughout his difficult journey. On top of that, he and his brothers were fully reconciled, with a depth of relationship they had never experienced as younger men.

4. Joseph accepted the realities he couldn't change. How do you think that affected his journey? If you were to accept your journey, how might it would affect you and the people around you?

5. Although God's ways are mysterious, how do you thing God might redeem your tears with regard to you present loss?

CONNECTING - 15 MINUTES

Accepting a loss, and choosing to stay in our pain our responses to loss can be very emotional and complex. When we accept the realities of our loss and risk asking God the hard questions, He will meet us in our pain and enable us to come to terms with our grief and find peace.

1. At this point in your grief process, where are you with regard to accepting the realities of your loss?

1	2	3	4	5	6	7	8	9	10
I still have "why" questions I must have answered			I'm on the path; I just need a little space and time				I am asking God how He plans to redeem my loss		

The *Serenity Prayer*, written by Reinhold Niebuhr, depicts perfectly the attitude we should all be striving for at this point in our journey. Let's read it in unison as our prayer today.

GOD GRANT ME THE SERENITY
TO ACCEPT THE THINGS I CANNOT CHANGE;
COURAGE TO CHANGE THE THINGS I CAN;
AND WISDOM TO KNOW THE DIFFERENCE.
LIVING ONE DAY AT A TIME;

ENJOYING ONE MOMENT AT A TIME;
ACCEPTING HARDSHIPS AS THE PATHWAY TO PEACE;
TAKING, AS HE DID, THIS SINFUL WORLD
AS IT IS, NOT AS I WOULD HAVE IT;
TRUSTING THAT HE WILL MAKE ALL THINGS RIGHT
IF I SURRENDER TO HIS WILL;
THAT I MAY BE REASONABLY HAPPY IN THIS LIFE
AND SUPREMELY HAPPY WITH HIM
FOREVER IN THE NEXT.
AMEN.

2. What can this group do this week in a practical way to help you come to terms with accepting your journey? How can we pray for you today?

MY PRAYER REQUESTS:

MY GROUP'S PRAYER REQUESTS:

In addition to specific prayer requests, pray together for each person individually, that he or she would begin see that God is present, feeling the pain, and wanting so much to help with this journey.

TAKING IT HOME

LOOKING INWARD ... A QUESTION TO TAKE TO MY HEART:

Look into your heart for what beliefs about God, yourself, and the world around you are driving your attitudes and behavior.

If you rated yourself below a "5" on question 1 above, ask your heart:

> ✳ "Why am I'm still getting stuck? What are the things that I really believe about God, about myself, about others, and about my life that are hanging me up? "

If you rated yourself "5" or higher on question 1 above, ask your heart:

> ✳ "Am I rushing the process and perhaps pretending things are making sense when they don't, or am I really beginning to accept my journey as it is and allowing God to walk with me?"

Looking Upward ... A Question to Take to God:

Take this question to God this week and wait on His response. Don't try to anticipate what He will say based on the Bible. Wait for Him to speak personally in a fresh way.

> ✳ "God, what are You up to in my life? What is it that You're trying to do in my life and through my life in the aftermath of this loss?"

Looking Forward ... Prepare for Session 6:

Please capture your thoughts and feelings on the following journal page as you work through your grief and healing process. Consider these questions that will be discussed in Session 6.

(1) When I'm still and quiet, what are some things that I still cannot accept?
(2) Who could I talk to this week to help me understand where I am in my grief?
(3) Who am I blaming or angry with? Is there anyone I need to forgive and release from blame?
(4) What guilt or shame might I be carrying? For what things do I need to seek and accept God's forgiveness? 1 John 1:9 promises that, "If we confess our sins, He is faithful and righteous to forgive our sins and cleanse us from unrighteousness."

Acceptance Journal

CONNECTING WITH HELP: GOD

One of the key threads running through our *Redeeming the Tears* study has been the importance of listening to our hearts to surface what we really believe about God. At the same time, we've been asking God to reveal how He feels about each of us personally, and what He was doing during and after our loss. Within the context of the larger story, we've begun to position the event of our loss, listen to and realign our hearts, accept the realities of our lives, and commit to moving ahead.

Until we've wrestled with and settled the issue about the goodness and love of God, we will struggle to dismantle the wall that blocks our progress. Once we settle the "God issue," we can face our fears as we rely on Him to reveal one by one the lies we have embraced. As the Holy Spirit reveals and replace sour false agreements and vows with truth, we will experience freedom, rest, and peace. God wants us to take our messy lives to Him.

OBJECTIVES FOR THIS SESSION:
• Find that the way to God is "down" as we invite Him into our pain and grief
• Introduce the spiritual discipline of grieving
• Experience a personal touch from God
• Begin to dismantle the false agreements and vows that are attached to our losses
• Find hope in the power of replacing lies with truth

BREAKING THE ICE - 10 MINUTES

LEADER: *It's now week six of the study and your group has shared a lot together. These "Breaking the Ice" questions should be a fun way to continue getting to know each other and launch the topic for today. Encourage everyone to participate in responding to the questions, but keep things moving.*

1. Most teenagers are embarrassed by their parents at some point. Tell us what your parents did that was embarrassing to you. This could be an experience, something they wore, something they said to you, a habit, etc.

2. When you were a child, what was the most exciting outing you had with your father or someone who was a father figure to you? How old were you when you last shared this kind of time with him?

❐ Fishing
❐ Shopping
❐ Playing baseball
❐ Dates with Dad
❐ Going to an amusement park together
❐ Swimming
❐ Other:

3. When you were a child, what was the most frightening thing to you? Who did you run to that made you feel safe when you experienced that fear?

OPENING PRAYER

God, we seek You in this journey tonight. We're all grown up but there are many times in life when we need someone bigger that we can trust; someone we can reach out to for help and comfort as we try to make sense of our lives. Come and show us Your love today.

OUR ROAD MAP - 15 MINUTES

A P.L.A.C.E. FOR THE HURT

POSITION THE EVENT:	What place does your loss have in your life's journey? Connect your memories of that moment and your emotions.
LISTEN TO YOUR HEART:	What does your heart tell you about yourself and the event?
ACCEPT YOUR JOURNEY:	What realities cannot be changed? Will you press on?
► CONNECT WITH HELP:	Will you reach out to God and other people for help?
EMBRACE REDEMPTION:	Are you ready to redeem your tears? Allow God to empower you to return to living life and to become a conduit for His healing work in others.

In the last session, we made progress toward "accepting our journeys." As we acknowledge and accept the realities that we cannot change, and commit to move forward with faith and courage, we are freed to reach out for help. Connecting with the help we need is harder than it sounds. There are often barriers in our hearts and minds that would keep us isolated. But the benefits of breaking out of our ruts provide hope to reach up and out.

1. How did your "Taking it Home" assignments go? Would you share any insight you gained about getting stuck and the beliefs that hang you up?

2. Did you hear from God about how He might redeem your tears?

Your homework was to ponder the following questions:
(1) When I'm still and quiet, what are some things that I still cannot accept?
(2) Who could I talk to this week to help me understand where I am in my grief?
(3) Who am blaming or angry with? Is there anyone I need to forgive and release from blame?
(4) What guilt or shame might I be carrying? For what things do I need to seek and accept God's forgiveness? 1 John 1:9 promises that, "If we confess our sins, He is faithful and righteous to forgive our sins and cleanse us from unrighteousness."

4. Is there someone who you've blamed or are angry with about your loss? As you've listened to your heart and to God, do you think these are people you need to forgive?

5. Are you carrying any guilt? If so, what do you think is preventing you from experiencing God's grace and forgiveness?

6. Again, let's turn to your "How ya' doin' really?" page inside the back cover of your book. Put today's date next to Week 6 along with the rating that best describes your emotional state right now.

DISCOVERING THE TRUTH - 30 MINUTES

This week we're going to focus on the first step of "C"—"connecting with God for help."

BARRIERS TO CONNECTING WITH HELP

What is it about us that keeps us from connecting with those who can help us even when we're hurting? The following descriptions may provide us clues about why we might be going it alone.

* *Private Eye: "I'm a very private person."*
Some of us keep everything private either because our parents taught us that it isn't appropriate to discuss personal matters, or just because we are introverts.

* *Whatever: "It won't do me any good any way."*
Some of us deny the source of relief because we don't believe God is willing to help us. Because we don't believe God cares enough to help, we don't ask for His assistance or the help of others.

* *Minnie Me: "It's not that big of a deal."*
Some of us minimize the importance of our grief. We have eluded our true feelings by convincing ourselves that our loss or pain is part of life and so it's no big deal.

* *The Great Wall: "I just can't get past my anger."*
To be whole, a grieving person must release his or her anger. Some of us bottle up the anger we're feeling and erect a protective wall around our hearts. From the outside we appear fine, but in truth we're burning up from the inside out. Until we are willing to remove that wall so the anger can be released, we will never experience peace.

* *The Lone Ranger: "I can make it on my own."*
Reaching out for help is not typically encouraged or rewarded in our culture of rugged individualism. Some of us choose to be dangerously independent. We portray the illusion of strength while inside we're hurting deeply. Sooner or later the emotions will surface causing us to "hit the wall" even harder.

4. Which of these descriptions for going it alone might you be prone to use? The enemy's plan is to isolate us and then take us out. What can we do about this?

Some of us believe the lie that God sends pain to punish us, while others believe that God doesn't "give a rip" about what we are going through. The truth is that God understands every pain we experience. When we look to the things of this world for fulfillment, even things that look good, we will always find pain and always be left wanting. Only God can heal our pain and set us free.

LEADER: Ask two different members of your group to read the passages from Jeremiah and Genesis.

Let's see how God looks at our pain and losses.

[God speaking:] They dress the wound of my people as though it is not serious. "Peace, peace," they say, when there is no peace.

JEREMIAH 6:14 (NASB)

1. What do these words reveal about God's interest in us and His focus of our hurts? Does He focus on symptoms or causes? Why would that be better?

GOD'S CARE FOR HURTING PEOPLE

Abram and Sarai could not have children and they were aging; yet God had promised to bless the world through their descendants. They were in a serious quandary. What could they do? In her impatience, Sarai convinced Abram to sleep with their slave, Hagar. Once the servant girl became pregnant, there was nothing but envy between the two women. They couldn't stand to look at each other. This confrontation forced Hagar into a desperate place where God found her. Check it out.

⁶ Abram replied to Sarai, "Here, your slave is in your hands; do whatever you want with her." Then Sarai mistreated her so much that she ran away from her. ⁷ The Angel of the Lord found her by a spring of water in the wilderness, the spring on the way to Shur. ⁸ He said, "Hagar, slave of Sarai, where have you come from, and where are you going?"

She replied, "I'm running away from my mistress Sarai."

⁹ Then the Angel of the Lord said to her, "You must go back to your mistress and submit to her mistreatment." ¹⁰ The Angel of the Lord also said to her, "I will greatly multiply your offspring, and they will be too many to count." ¹¹ Then the Angel of the Lord said to her: You have conceived and will have a son. You will name him Ishmael, for the Lord has heard your [cry of] affliction.

GENESIS 16:6-11

1. Why do you think God would just stand there and let Sarai to mistreat Hagar?

2. What circumstances have you faced or are you facing that lead you to believe that God is allowing you to be know pain?

3. Why do you think God gave Hagar direction, hope, and a promise?
   ❏ Pity Party: He felt sorry for her
   ❏ Love, Love, Love: He loved her like He loves everyone
   ❏ Redeeming the Tears: God turns bad situations into something good
   ❏ The Larger Story: Because He had a greater plan than Hagar could imagine
   ❏ Other: _____ .

EMBRACING THE TRUTH - 20 MINUTES

> LEADER: This section will help your group members begin to integrate the truths from Hagar's life into their own journeys. You will also encourage each other to join with God in demolishing the strongholds in your lives. Invite various group members to read the Scripture verses in this section.

1. God sent help to Hagar while she was in a difficult situation. Do you believe God is willing to be with you in your difficult situation? Why or why not?

As we accept that God really does care deeply for us and draw near to Him, His Spirit will help us dismantle our walls and move toward freedom.

³ For although we are walking in the flesh, we do not wage war in a fleshly way, ⁴ since the weapons of our warfare are not fleshly, but are powerful through God for the demolition of strongholds. We demolish arguments ⁵ and every high-minded thing that is raised up [or exalts itself] against the knowledge of God, taking every thought captive to the obedience of Christ.

2 CORINTHIANS 10:3-5

Do not be conformed to this world, but be transformed by the renewing of your mind, so that you may prove [that is discern] what the will of God is, that which is good and acceptable and perfect.

ROMANS 12:2 (NASB)

³¹ So Jesus said to the Jews who had believed Him, "If you continue in My word, you really are My disciples. ³² You will know the truth, and the truth will set you free."

JOHN 8:31-32

2. How can we demolish the "strongholds" in our lives, those beliefs that hold us captive?

3. What do these verses indicate is the spiritual battleground? We often already know the truth intellectually, but how can we know the truth in our hearts and innermost beings?

CONNECTING - 15 MINUTES

LEADER: Again, continue to keep what remains of the stack of bricks and the metal garbage can from Session 3 available for your group members. If anyone is ready this week to remove the first brick from his or her wall, they may grab a brick, and toss it into the garbage can. Use this "Connecting" time to develop a sense of community in your group as people strengthen their connection with God. Those still wrestling with God about foundational issues may feel like they are not as spiritual as others who are not wrestling. Remind them of the story of Jacob and God's pleasure in our wrestling with Him. Be sensitive to each person's place in his or her journey.

Often, we already know the truth intellectually, but as we encounter God Himself, He dispels our lies. He is the light and truth. Let's join in another personal encounter.

LEADER INSTRUCTIONS FOR GROUP EXPERIENCE: See page 120 also.
Turn down the lights in the room, and relight the menorah or three-place candleholder from Session 1 to symbolize the presence of God. With the room dark or dim, ask your group members to close their eyes. Say this: "As we have used the candles to represent the presence of God, close your eyes and envision God the Father, God the Son, and God the Holy Spirit walking into this room now. As they approach you, how do you feel? What is going through your mind?"

After a pause, say this: "Many of us feel panicked or nervous, unsure whether we are good enough to be accepted. Or perhaps we even expect God to lash out at us for what we've done. But that's a lie from the lips of the enemy! The truth is that God created you in His image, and He not only loves you, but He truly enjoys you. The Father sent the Son to die in our place so we could regain our original glory. The Holy Spirit absolutely enjoys coming alongside to help you. In fact, as the awesome Trinity enters the room, what they really do is rush to your side, kneel down, and embrace you.

Pass out the candles you brought, one to each group member, and then read the steps and questions below:

1. Your candle represents your life, which God longs to rescue from "the domain of darkness" (Colossians 1:13), enabling you to walk in His light. Come forward one at a time, and recognize God is the source of light in our darkness. It is only as you encounter Him personally, and touch your candle to His light that truth ignites in your heart.

2. Once each person has lighted his or her candle, gather together in a circle. Notice that the intensity of the light increases as you draw closer together. That's the reality of Christian community.

3. What has God revealed to you today? What are specific ways that we can pray for you and support you this week?

My Prayer Requests:

My Group's Prayer Requests:

In addition to specific prayer requests, thank God for His love and His light. Ask Him to continue to reveal Himself to you.

Taking it Home

Looking Inward ... A Question to Take to My Heart:

Look into your heart for what beliefs about God, yourself, and the world around you are driving your attitudes and behavior..

＊ Do I have a greater sense of God's nearness at this point in my journey? Am I pushing Him away or embracing Him? What is the real reason for my response to God?

Looking Upward ... A Question to Take to God:

Take this question to God this week and wait on His response. Don't try to anticipate what He will say based on the Bible. Wait for Him to speak personally in a fresh way.

✳ Holy Spirit, I invite you into my pain. Would you help me to tear down the enemy's strongholds and lies?

Looking Forward ... Prepare for Session 7:

Please capture your thoughts and feelings on the following journal page as you work through your grief and healing process. Consider these questions that will be discussed in Session 7:

(1) How can I know that God is trustworthy?

(2) How can I deepen my relationship with God?

(3) What would help me to be more willing to connect with other people for help? What would encourage me to connect with other people to help them?

Connection and Truth Journal

CONNECTING WITH HELP: COMMUNITY

Our time of connection in our last session was a meaningful experience as we sought a personal encounter with God. God cares deeply for each of us, and He wants us to fully embrace Him, but He welcomes and even looks forward to our struggles with Him as we search for truth. As we began our journey together several weeks ago, we acknowledged that healing occurs best in the context of community.

God is relational and created us to live in relationship with Him and each other. One key aspect of making sense of our journeys is seeing ourselves through the eyes of others. Sharing our stories with each other, lifting one another up, and cheering one another on in our journeys are also vital. In fact, as deeper community develops, our individual journeys merge into a single community journey. God has a purpose in our journey together. He's building us into a redemptive community, one in which we share our lives and struggles as we join God in His mission of setting us free from the lies we embrace that are holding us captive. The amazing power of community is that as we connect with other people for help, we also end up helping them in the process.

OBJECTIVES FOR THIS SESSION:
- Deepen our understanding of community and its benefits
- Understand some of the essentials of authentic community
- Embrace the power of community in our grieving process
- Continue to open up more in this group and in our other relationships

BREAKING THE ICE - 10 MINUTES

LEADER: *The "Breaking the Ice" questions for this session focus on the importance of supportive relationships. They encourage people to consider what they value in friends and have some fun in the process.*

1. If you were a participant on the *Fear Factor* show, what would be your greatest fear?
   - ❏ Laying in a container full of poisonous snakes
   - ❏ Having my face covered with spiders
   - ❏ Diving for rings in a pool full of jellyfish
   - ❏ Walking across a ladder suspended 200 feet in the air
   - ❏ Driving a car off a cliff while blindfolded
   - ❏ Eating 100-year-old rotten pig brains
   - ❏ Other: _____

2. The *Fear Factor* program allows participants to choose a partner they trust who helps them overcome their fears and move toward action. If you had to experience the fear you identified in question 1, which friend would you want by your side and why?

3. Who was your best friend in high school or college? What values did that person live out that caused you to hold them in high esteem?

OPENING PRAYER

God, we have begun to develop friendships within this group. Just as we need to invite You into our journey through grief, we also need to develop the support of a community of fellow travelers. Help us to allow the people in this group to have access to our lives. We sincerely want to deepen our experience of community with each other.

Our Road Map - 15 minutes

A P.L.A.C.E. FOR THE HURT

Position the event: What place does your loss have in your life's journey? Connect your memories of that moment and your emotions.

Listen to your heart: What does your heart tell you about yourself and the event?

Accept your journey: What realities cannot be changed? Will you press on?

► **Connect with help:** Will you reach out to God and other people for help?

Embrace redemption: Are you ready to redeem your tears? Allow God to empower you to return to living life and to become a conduit for His healing work in others.

In the last session, we made further strides in "connecting with God." We acknowledged that connecting with the help we need is harder than it sounds. God has placed specific people in our lives to support us in our struggles. Just as we need to invite God into our pain, we also need to allow other people access to our grief and our hearts. As we continue to open our lives and hearts to each other, everyone benefits. Of course this has risks, but the risks are much greater if we try to go it alone.

1. How did your "Taking it Home" assignments go? How is your relationship with God really going? Are you still wrestling with Him? If so, how can we encourage you to stay at it? Are you inviting Him into your pain?

2. What lies, agreements, and vows are surfacing as you ask your heart and God the hard questions? Have there been any freeing truths that the Spirit is revealing and illuminating for you? Please share them with the group.

Your homework was to ponder the following questions:

(1) How can I know that God is trustworthy?

(2) How can I deepen my relationship with God?

(3) What would help me to be more willing to connect with other people for help? What would encourage me to connect with other people to help them?

3. How can we know that we can trust God and fully depend on Him? How can we deepen our current relationship with God?

4. Again, let's turn to your "How ya' doin' really?" page inside the back cover of your book. Put today's date next to Week 7 along with the rating that best describes your emotional state right now..

DISCOVERING THE TRUTH - 35 MINUTES

When Christ-followers are hurting, we should be naturally drawn to one another. That's the second part of the "C"—"connecting with other people in community." We'll re-count the moments But too often we believe that, with God on our side, we can handle anything. The musical *Carousel* is the story of a young girl whose father had committed murder and then died before she was born. Throughout her life, this young girl struggled with loneliness. At some point she realized that the spirit of her father was with her and would be with her the rest of her life. She joyfully sang these lyrics:

When you walk through a storm hold your head up high
And don't be afraid of the dark.
At the end of the storm is a golden sky and the sweet silver song of a lark.
Walk on through the wind. Walk on through the rain though your dreams be tossed and blown. Walk on, walk on with hope in your heart and you'll never walk alone. You'll never walk alone!

Like this girl, some of us believe that if the Father is with us, we should be whole. We resolutely believe that we can make it through all of life's storms as long as God is with us. But that's never been God's plan. God's plan has always been that we walk through life with Him at work in us and with people on either side of us helping to carry the burdens of life. As a connected community, we work in tandem with God to help each other through difficult times and together celebrate triumphs.

WHAT IS COMMUNITY?

The word "community" is derived from the root word for "common," so a community is a group of people who share things in common. Community is more than sharing a zip code; it is sharing our stories, our journeys, and our lives.

1. What life experiences, interests, and passions have you discovered that you share with others in your group?

2. One of the greatest gifts people can give is the gift of their time and undivided attention. Share a time when another person came alongside you and said, "I know this situation is difficult for you, so I've cleared off my calendar and I'm here for you. My day is yours." How did that gift make you feel?

3. What experiences have you shared in this group that brought you closer together? In what ways has this community benefited you?

WHAT IS THE ENVIRONMENT FOR AUTHENTIC COMMUNITY?

The people in this group came together at this time to deal with the same essential issue, so we are uniquely equipped to help one another. While it may have gone unnoticed, this group has become progressively more unified over the course of several weeks. Here are some key aspects of community:

A secure harbor from life's storms: As we've journeyed together through grief and loss, we have built a confidential relationship where we are safe to be ourselves and share what's really going on with us.

A place to share our stories: In our brief time together, we've enjoyed many opportunities to tell our stories and learn from the stories of others. This is a rarity in our busy culture.

Perspective: People who have known us even for a brief time can see what I cannot see in any given circumstance or moment.

Practical assistance: We have helped each other in practical ways to stay in the battle, and to express our thoughts and feelings about our situations so we could begin to position our event or loss in our lives and in the larger story.

Acceptance: During our times together, if we've wanted to, we have been able to express our honest reactions to what has happened in our lives. As people engaged in our own journeys, we have tried to listen without criticism or condemnation.

Support and encouragement: Our ability to stand firm in difficulties and press on despite significant challenges and opposition has been enhanced by the collective strength of our group.

Accountability: Proverbs 27:17 says, "Iron sharpens iron, and one man sharpens another." This highlights that when one friend challenges another and lovingly questions motives, actions, and activities, it may be a little hard to take, but it does help to mold and strengthen the other. As caring friends, we can point out times when the other might need to change directions in our thinking, approach to God, or approach to life.

4. Which of these aspects of community has been most helpful to you and why?

LEADER: Ask various group members to read the Bible story and teaching passages. Encourage everyone to participate in the Bible discovery questions.

THE POWER OF COMMUNITY

We have learned the vital importance of wrestling with God until He comes and personally addresses my issue. Reaching out to God in total dependence is necessary if we are going to defeat the enemy of our souls and demolish the strongholds in our lives. But what happens when our arms get tired, or when we fall down, or when our burdens become too heavy for us? Community is really a simple concept, and yet powerful in its effect. Let's look into some examples from the Bible.

8 At Rephidim, Amalek came and fought against Israel. 9 Moses said to Joshua, "Select some men for us, and go fight against Amalek. Tomorrow I will stand on the hilltop with God's staff in my hand." 10 Joshua did as Moses had told him, and fought against Amalek, while Moses, Aaron, and Hur went up to the top of the hill. 11 While Moses held up his hand, Israel prevailed, but whenever he put his hand down, Amalek prevailed. 12 When Moses' hands grew heavy, they took a stone and put [it] under him, and he sat down on it. Then Aaron and Hur supported his hands, one on one side and one on the other so that his hands remained steady until the sun went down. 12 So Joshua defeated Amalek and his army with the sword.

EXODUS 17:8-13

5. Why do you think Moses stood on the hilltop with "God's staff" in his hands during Amalek's battle against the Israelites? Why wasn't he engaged in the battle on the ground?

6. What was the significance of Moses holding his hands up? What weapon(s) are available to us today with the same power as the raising of "God's staff"?

7. What happened in the battle whenever Moses got tired or worn out from reaching up? What would the outcome have been if Aaron and Hur had ignored his need? What would have happened if Moses had insisted on handling his own struggles when Aaron and Hur began to help him?

8. What do you think went through Moses' mind when these guys came alongside him and brought strength to powerless muscles? As the Israelites looked up from their fighting, what do you think watching these three men did for them in their own battles?

9. No doubt both Aaron's arms and Hur's arms became tired and weak as the battle continued. Why do you think they continued to join Moses in his struggle even when they
were experiencing pain and weakness?

EMBRACING THE TRUTH - 15 MINUTES

*LEADER: This section will help your group members begin to integrate the truths they have dis-
covered about community into their own lives. Encourage everyone to give their perspectives on the
questions.*

We've learned some great lessons about the importance of standing together as a connected community in our grief and struggles. Let's discuss how we might apply these
lessons to our own situations.

*⁹ Two are better than one because they have a good reward for their efforts: ¹⁰ If either falls down, his
companion can lift him up; but pity the one who falls without another to lift him up. ¹¹ Also, if two
lie down together, they can keep warm; but how can one person alone keep warm? ¹² And if somebody
overpowers, one person, two can resist him. A cord of three strands is not easily broken.*

ECCLESIASTES 4:9-12

1. If we choose to grieve alone, why are we more vulnerable when the enemy attacks?
How might you get stuck or diverted in your grieving journey if you choose to go it
alone? What advantages do you see when a committed community stands with you in
your grief and struggles?

2. In what practical ways have other people helped you during the early weeks of your loss? How did that make you feel?
   - ❏ Bringing food for me and/or my family to eat
   - ❏ Listening to me when I needed to vent
   - ❏ Taking care of my yard
   - ❏ Baby-sitting my children
   - ❏ Sitting silently with me (the gift of presence)
   - ❏ Other: _____

3. We described authentic community as a "safe" environment in which we are free to be ourselves and share what's really going on with us. In your opinion, what characteristics would a "safe" person exhibit?

4. You may feel that your load is too heavy to carry right now. You're probably right. Apart from God, whom would you choose to hold you up or help carry your burden? Why would you choose that person?

Openness and honesty are vital if we're going to help each other to grieve, tear down strongholds, replace lies with truth, and find healing. Openness requires risk and vulnerability, but if we treat each other as members of the same body, we will find added strength.

Therefore, laying aside falsehood, SPEAK TRUTH EACH ONE of you WITH HIS NEIGHBOR, for we are members of one another.

EPHESIANS 4:25 (NASB)

5. At this point in your grieving process, where are you with regard to opening up and sharing what's really going on inside you with the people you're closest to?

1	2	3	4	5	6	7	8	9	10
I could never share what's going on inside me with someone			I'm still holding back, but I'm beginning to open up					I am completely open about everything	

CONNECTING - 15 MINUTES

We've learned that community is a powerful idea, but it requires something of us. Just as we need to invite God into our grief and pain, we also need to allow other people access to our lives. To build redemptive community with other people requires that together we take the risk of opening our lives and hearts to each other. As we continue to open up and share each other's burdens, our individual journeys merge into a single journey. God's purpose in community is redemption. He wants us to share our lives and struggles so that we join in His mission to set us free from the secrets and lies we embrace that are holding us captive ... keeping us stuck.

1. Take turns responding to the following question: What's the most inspiring experience you've had during our journey together so far?

2. Take turns sharing another memory. Looking back over our time together as a group, what is the most humorous thing you can recall happening?

3. How can this group help you to feel comfortable as we make efforts to reach out to each other this week? How can we pray for you today?

My Prayer Requests:

My Group's Prayer Requests:

In addition to specific prayer requests, thank God for bringing each individual to join this group and for the experiences you have shared together.

The next meeting "A Night to Remember" will be very unique experience. You won't want to miss it.

Preparation: Think about EACH person in your group. Spend time thinking a jotting down quick notes related two questions:

(1) What has this person done for you during the time this group has been together? Ideas: helpful statements, encouraging story, a practical need met, a hug or word of encouragement, etc.

(2) What does this person have to offer? Ideas: abilities, as yet unaccomplished personal goals and dreams, personality or character traits, spiritual gifts, etc.

Taking it Home

Looking Inward ... A Question to Take to My Heart:

Look back at the "Embracing the Truth" section to the scale related to opening up and sharing what's really going on inside you with the people you're closest to?

If you rated yourself "5" or below on that scale, ask your heart:

> ✳ "Why would I be holding back from people who could help me in
> my journey? What am I worried will happen if people get to see the
> real me?"

If you rated yourself higher than a "5" on the question above, ask your heart:

> ✳ Are there any vows or beliefs (Psalm 51:6 NASB) that are driving
> distrust or a protective posture for me with other people?" What
> prevents me from fully removing my "mask"?

Looking Upward ... A Question to Take to God:

> ✳ "Jesus, I know You want me to connect with other people for help.
> Would You show me how You really see me as a person? Are there
> other people that You want me to connect with so that we can help
> each other in our current struggles? "

Looking Forward ... Preparation for Session 8:

Please capture your thoughts and feelings on the following journal page as you work
through your grief and healing process. Consider these questions that will be discussed in
our final session (after we get together for "A Night to Remember"):

(1) Who has been the most helpful person to you so far in my journey? Have you shared
with him or her how grateful you are?

(2) Where do you see yourself on the P.L.A.C.E. road map at this point in time? Do you
have a clearer sense of where you're going and how you might get there?

(3) Would you like to stay connected with this group as you continue your journey
through grief and loss? How much contact would be helpful and comfortable for you?

Connection Journal

A Night to Remember

Drowning a part of ourselves in the pool of grief is normal. It's easy to become overwhelmed by our pain so that we become defined by our loss. We may develop tunnel vision, able to focus only on our loss and/or the false self the enemy wants us believe we have become. We may have forgotten that we are more than our grief; that we have a great deal in our hearts and lives to offer people God places in our path. Our sorrow can desensitize us, making us numb to our uniqueness and value to others.

Today we're going to help one another remove the blinders and pull each another out of the pool. We're going to experience the benefit of seeing ourselves through the eyes of others.

Breaking the Ice

1. When you were in high school or college what would your closest friends say you were best at?
   - ❏ Sports (if so, what sport?)
   - ❏ Drama
   - ❏ Making great grades (what was your grade point average?)
   - ❏ Music (if so what instrument did you play or what part did you sing?)
   - ❏ Art
   - ❏ Other: _____

2. Prior to your loss, what activity did you find the greatest pleasure in?

CONNECTING

EXPERIENCE 1: SEEING OURSELVES THROUGH THE EYES OF GOD

Part of the journey toward healing is remembering who you are, that you are a person of unparalleled worth ... unparalleled, because there is no one like you. God made one wonderful unique you, then He stepped back, took a look, and, as is true of everything He has ever created, came to an amazing and affirming realization that you are good.

Let's meditate on what happened after God created you. Here's what the Bible says happened when God created the earth: "God saw all that He had made, and it was very good" (Genesis 1:31a). Because you are His creation you are good. But what do you think His reaction was the first time He saw you after you were created?

Take 60 seconds to look at yourself through the eyes of God and envision what His reaction was when He saw the wonder and uniqueness He created in you. Close your eyes and watch His reaction.

1. What did you see as you visualized the scene of your creation? How did God react when He saw you for the first time? Share this with the group.

EXPERIENCE 2: SEEING OURSELVES THROUGH THE EYES OF OTHERS

LEADER: *Explain this experience to your group members, and ask them to help you set up the chairs. You will have to direct each person to the "vision seat" because few will volunteer to be next. Carefully monitor and manage your time so everyone gets his or her turn for affirmation. You'll want to limit the time to only 5 minutes for each person, splitting the time equally between the two discussion points. IMPORTANT: Ensure someone in the group assumes the role of writing what is shared for each person affirmed. This role should be shared among members of the group with legible handwriting.*

Affirmation is a powerful tool that only God uses. Satan despises affirmation because, when we affirm one another, strongholds are broken and lies displaced. Perhaps this is one of the reasons Paul wrote, "Encourage one another and build each other up, just as in fact you are doing" (1 Thessalonians 5:11 NIV).

Let's join God in affirming one another right now. Gather all of the chairs (except one) into a half circle. Take one chair and put it in front of the rest with the back of that chair facing the other chairs. One person will sit in this chair while the rest of the group sits in the half circle area. Each person in the group will take a turn in the "vision seat."

The person in the "vision seat" is going to listen in as others talk about them. In most settings when people talk behind our backs they say negative things. In this experience we're going to say positive things about the person in the chair.

In order to make this a significant, memorable experience, one person will write down each statement of affirmation shared about the person in the "vision seat." There's a place in each of our books for these statements to be written down. One person should take the book of the person in the special seat and chronicle what is being shared. In this way each person will walk away with a record of the wonderful characteristics they may have never noted or not been able to see in themselves to this point. You'll have five minutes for each person.

IMPORTANT: The person in the vision seat may not say anything, turn toward the group speaking about them, or gesture. Some people are not use to the gift of affirmation being given them. Their response is to find some way to deflect these statements rather than welcome these wonderful words to their hearts, where transformation occurs.

SPEND TWO AND A HALF MINUTES FOCUSING ON EACH OF THE FOLLOWING AREAS (5 MINUTES TOTAL FOR EACH PERSON):

1. WHAT THIS PERSON HAS DONE FOR ME. People in the group will tell one another what the person in the special chair has done for them during the time this group has been together. This could include a statement made during group time that helped in the journey, a practical need he or she met, a hug or word of encouragement given at a much needed time, etc. Words of thanks may be spoken at this time also.

2. WHAT THIS PERSON HAS TO OFFER. People in the group will tell one another what the person in the special chair has to offer himself or herself, others, and the world on the other side of the grief process. This could include, abilities, as yet unaccomplished personal goals and dreams, personality or character traits, spiritual gifts, etc.

Experience 3: Embracing the Truth

Each person should read over his or her own list and choose 2 items from the list that were especially encouraging or inspiring. Each person will take a turn reading aloud the two special items. As each person finishes, the group leader will bless him or her individually by reciting this verse:

The Lord your God is with you,
*   he is mighty to save.*
* He will take great delight in you,*
*   he will quiet you with his love,*
*   he will rejoice over you with singing.*
Zephaniah. 3:17 (NIV)

> LEADER: *Encourage each person in the group to take the list they have been given and place it in a location where it will be seen daily. These lists will serve as reminders of God's beauty in them and visions that their futures are going to be fantastic adventures.*

Close by reading this prayer together in unison ...

We praise You God because we were "remarkably and wonderfully made;" and "Your works are wonderful," we "know this very well" (Psalm 139:14 HCSB). And because You created each of us for a purpose, we know you have a plan for us: "plans to prosper" us " and not to harm" us, "plans to give" us "hope and a future" (Jeremiah 29:11 NIV). Amen.

A Night to Remember—Memories

EMBRACING REDEMPTION

Perhaps our experience of "A Night to Remember" was a turning point for some of us. Seeing ourselves through the eyes of God and the eyes of others helps us keep a proper perspective as we journey through grief and pain. Our group has covered a lot of ground over this brief time of redeeming our tears together. Just understanding the road map we need to follow is a huge step. In this final session we will focus on continuing our journeys and discuss the destination in order to motivate you to stay on your journey.

Even though this is the last session in our study, it is by no means the end of our grieving journeys. We can celebrate our breakthroughs and progress, but our real goal should be to embrace hope.

OBJECTIVES FOR THIS SESSION:
- Learn healthy habits for continued recovery
- Develop a spirit of anticipation for what God will do; Embrace hope
- Gain a fresh view into who God is and release our burdens to Him
- Deepen our understanding of God's love for us
- Grasp a vision for our parts in the larger story

BREAKING THE ICE - 10 MINUTES

LEADER: *The "Breaking the Ice" questions will help your group members to look to the future.*

1. As I look to the future I feel most like:
   - ❏ Spiderman – I can climb over the wall of despair.
   - ❏ Wonder Woman – I can dodge the arrows Satan is launching at me.
   - ❏ Superman – I'm concerned kryptonite may be just around the corner.
   - ❏ Batman – Sometimes I want to hide in my cave.
   - ❏ Underdog – You may be surprised, but I will overcome.
   - ❏ Other: _____.

2. Who was the person you turned to in high school or college when you were going through hard times? What was this person's primary influence in your life? If he or she were sitting in the room with you right now what would you say to them? (Finish this sentence: "Thank you for ...)

OPENING PRAYER:

God, we have come to understand that grieving is a process that will take time. We have begun to experience You and Your truth in profound ways and we have embraced your life-sustaining gift of hope. As we continue our journeys, grant each of us the determination to never give up, the courage to confront the enemy, and the passion to come alongside others who are willing to take this journey themselves.

OUR ROAD MAP - 15 MINUTES

A P.L.A.C.E. FOR THE HURT

POSITION THE EVENT: What place does your loss have in your life's journey? Connect your memories of that moment and your emotions.

LISTEN TO YOUR HEART: What does your heart tell you about yourself and the event?

ACCEPT YOUR JOURNEY: What realities cannot be changed? Will you press on?

CONNECT WITH HELP: Will you reach out to God and other people for help?

► **EMBRACE REDEMPTION:** Are you ready to redeem your tears? Allow God to empower you to return to living life and to become a conduit for His healing work in others.

As we complete this key phase in our grief process, we want to build a foundation of hope and joy. We have discovered a P.L.A.C.E. for our hurt and we are experiencing some level of healing and comfort through wrestling with God and by connecting with each other. The final step in the journey when you arrive at that point is "E"—"embracing redemption."

1. How did your "Taking it Home" assignments go? Did God or your heart reveal anything about why you connect with other people the way you do?

Your homework assignment was to ponder the following questions. Let's discuss them.

2. Who has been the most helpful person to you so far in your journey? Have you shared with him or her how grateful you are?

3. Where do you see yourself on the P.L.A.C.E. road map at this point in time? Do you have a clearer sense of where you're going and how you might get there?

4. Would you like to stay connected with this group as you continue your journey through grief and loss? How much contact would be helpful and comfortable for you?

LEADER: *This would be a good time to suggest to the group that redemptive community has not had time to take root in only eight meetings together. Ask the group if they would consider keeping the group together for continued support and redemption. Pass around 3 x 5" cards so people can jot down their potential interest. Some of the group members may be open to the idea.*

If there are not enough to form a small group, refer these people to your pastor to connect them with a group. If you form a group, we suggest your next step would be to go through the Serendipity House study entitled Great Beginnings. *You may order this online at www.SerendipityHouse.com.*

As you ask each person to report progress on the scale in question 5, take the lead in congratulating each person for staying on the journey and for any gains they have made.

5. One last time, let's turn to your "How ya' doin' really?" page inside the back cover of your book. Put today's date next to Week 8 along with the rating that best describes your emotional state right now. How have you progressed? What number on the scale did you start with in Session 1? Where are you now? What was your highest rating?

DISCOVERING THE TRUTH - 25 MINUTES

> LEADER: *In the initial part of "Discovering the Truth," you will discuss behaviors and habits that your group members will need to make a part of their lives as they continue in their journeys. Ask for volunteers to read the various explanations for the behaviors. The focus of the discovery questions is on understanding the "destination" in our journeys through loss. Spend more time will be focused on the "Embracing the Truth" questions today. Leave 15 minutes for the "Connecting" time at the end of this final session.*

HEALTHY HABITS

There are certain behaviors and habits that are consistent with people who continue well after experiencing loss and making the journey through grief.

* *Take care of yourself:* Your grieving process is unique. No one can tell you exactly how to grieve, and no one will do your grieving for you. Be sure pay attention to your emotional, physical, and spiritual needs.

* *Continue to wrestle with God and your heart:* The enemy will continue to speak lies to you and try to raise doubts about God's goodness, about who you really are, about other people, and about your life and purpose. Continue to probe your heart and wrestle with God about your pain, doubts, and questions.

* *Process your feelings:* Those who do well in the long run, talk through their feelings. Talking to God is key, but developing and maintaining relationships with people you trust and share with will also help you immensely. Sharing emotions is essential to you arriving and continuing strong on the other side of your grief.

* *Continue to stay in your larger story:* As we live our daily lives, it's easy to refocus only on the immediate issues and struggles . It's important to remember that your loss and other circumstances in your life are things you are going through. Your loss is not the end of your story and it doesn't define who you are or what God plans to do in and through you.

* *Allow God to take care of you:* It's easy for us to circle back around and pick up the burdens we have handed over to God. God enjoys you and counts it a privilege to walk through your journey with you. Receive His love and fully trust Him. Keep laying down your burdens and let God take care of you..

Cultivate joy and anticipation: Laughing is natural medicine. Finding the humor in everyday situations is a great release. While it's also important for you to enjoy pleasant memories of people or important things you have lost, it's critical that you look forward with anticipation of what God will do. Embrace the hope of His redemption for you.

Share your story with others: By sharing your story with others, you can make an incredible difference in the life of another person as you help him or her journey through grief and loss. As you share the story of your journey with others, you will also be reminded of what God has done in your life.

1. Which of these healthy habits would you say are strengths for you? Which one is the greatest struggle for you and why?

LEADER: *Ask different group members to read the explanations and Bible passages. Encourage everyone to participate in the Bible discovery questions.*

ARRIVING AT OUR DESTINATION

Our journey—our adventure with God—never ends, but there is place from which we can look into our rearview mirrors and know that our journey through the darkest times of grief is behind us. You will know that you've embraced God's redemption when two hopes have become a reality: (1) You return to a sense of spiritual and emotional equilibrium; and (2) You become a conduit for God's healing work in others. Arriving at our destination does not mean we stop grieving. A daily discipline of grieving before God is healthy and beneficial to us.

RETURNING TO A SENSE OF NORMALCY AND EQUILIBRIUM

The Apostle Paul experienced a life of hardships, persecution, imprisonment, beatings, and even attempts to kill him because of his commitment to live in the larger story and share Jesus throughout the Roman Empire. King David also experienced a life full of intense difficulties. Both through their pain and grief found life and, more importantly the source of life.

⁶ For God, who said, "Light shall shine out of darkness"—He has shone in our hearts to give the light of the knowledge of God's glory in the face of Jesus Christ. ⁷ Now we have this treasure in clay jars, so that this extraordinary power may be from God and not from us. ⁸ We are pressured in every way but not crushed; we are perplexed but not in despair; ⁹ we are persecuted but not abandoned; we are struck down but not destroyed. ¹⁰ We always carry the death of Jesus in our body, so that the life of Jesus may also be revealed in our body. ¹¹ For we who live are always given over to death because of Jesus, so that Jesus' life may also be revealed in our mortal flesh.

2 Corinthians 4:6-11

Weeping may last for the night, But a shout of joy comes in the morning.

Psalm 30:5 (NASB)

2. The "clay jars" refer to how fragile we feel at times, emotionally or physically. Who and what make up the "treasure" that Paul says we have in those clay jars (verse 6)? Why do you think it is so valuable?

3. What core truths do you think Paul and David embraced that enabled them to experience intense pressure, confusion, persecution, and abuse without giving in to despair? What kept them going?

4. These two men held on in hope, despite feelings that were overwhelmed by grief and pain. As we follow Paul's example (verses 6-7, and 10-11) and David's example, where should we look for joy and life—real life—even in the midst of our struggles? What might this look like for you?

BECOMING A CONDUIT TO OTHERS FOR GOD'S HEALING

Embracing God and experiencing His life in a deeper and fresher way is only part of our recovery. The other part is accepting God's invitation to rejoin Him in the larger story. *³ Blessed be the God and Father of our Lord Jesus Christ, the Father of mercies and the God of all comfort. ⁴ He comforts us in all our affliction, so that we may be able to comfort those who are in any kind of affliction, through the comfort we ourselves receive from God. ⁵ For as the sufferings of Christ overflow to us, so our comfort overflows through Christ.*

2 CORINTHIANS 1:3-5

6. How is God the Father portrayed in this description? How does this portrayal compare to your deepest heart-beliefs about God?

7. How do you think our past wounds and brokenness enhance our usefulness to God in His work of healing the brokenhearted and setting captives free??

Jesus suffered more deeply than we could imagine when He took all the pain and evil of the world on Himself and died to redeem us. Verse 5 indicates that as we share our pain with others, we will receive an overabundance of comfort through Him.

8. Who do you know that is struggling and needs some of the overflow of the comfort and new life you are receiving from God? What are you personally willing to do to bring comfort to that person? As a group?

EMBRACING THE TRUTH - 25 MINUTES

God has made some amazing promises to us if we are willing to raise our eyes to Him (above our current pain) and embrace the larger story. These promises give powerful incentive not to give up, but to continue fighting through the grief process. Let's see what God has in store for us.

Promised Rewards Awaiting Us

[16]Therefore we do not give up; even though our outer person is being destroyed, our inner person is being renewed day by day. [17]For our momentary light affliction is producing for us an absolutely incomparable eternal weight of glory. [18]So we do not focus on what is seen, but on what is unseen; for what is seen is temporary, but what is unseen is eternal.

2 Corinthians 4:16-18

1. What is God's promise in 2 Corinthians 4 if you do not give up? Does this promised reward excite you? How so or why not?

Satan continues to feed lies to us about God's goodness to force us into despair when God offers hope and abundance. His goal is to isolate, enslave, and destroy us. The truth is that Jesus brings incredible hope to all of us who are hurting or being held captive.

[This passage points to Jesus:] *[1]The Spirit of the Sovereign Lord is upon me to preach good news to the poor. He sent me to bind up the brokenhearted, to proclaim freedom for the captives and release from darkness for the prisoners, [2]to proclaim the year of the Lord's favor and the day of vengeance of our God, to comfort all who mourn, [3]to provide for those who grieve in Zion—to bestow on them the crown of beauty instead of ashes, the oil of gladness instead of mourning, and a garment of praise instead of a spirit of despair.*

Isaiah 61:1-3

2. Which of these characteristics described you when you joined this group? What words of hope and promise did you hear for yourself in this passage?
   - ❏ Poor
   - ❏ Brokenhearted
   - ❏ Captive
   - ❏ Imprisoned in darkness
   - ❏ Mourning
   - ❏ Despairing

3. Does it give you new hope as you grasp that Jesus wants to replace beauty for ashes, praise for despair, freedom for bondage and captivity, and light for darkness? Can you imagine playing a role in sharing this incredible news of freedom and redemption with others?

[God says:] "So I will restore to you the years that the swarming locust has eaten."

JOEL 2:25 (NKJV)

And we know that God causes all things to work together for good to those who love God, to those who are called according to His purpose.

ROMANS 8:28 (NASB)

4. Locusts often represent Satan's forces bringing torment or judgment into our lives. Locusts are ravenous, devouring life as they swarm. What does God promise our seasons of deep loss and grief?

5. What does Romans 8:28 say that God "causes"? Does He cause all things or does he have another purpose in mind for the painful events in our lives?

6. It's important to realize that God didn't plan our loss and He didn't desire it. We have an enemy and we live in a world with freedom of choice. According to Joel 2 and Romans 8, how is God restoring (redeeming) what the enemy meant for evil in our lives?

In Session 3 we saw Jacob wrestle long and hard with God until he prevailed over his pain and inner struggles. As a result, he received a new name (fresh start and identity), reconnection and intimacy with God, "deliverance" from his pain, a badge of honor—his limp. As wonderful as these gifts sound, God doesn't stop with that.

² Nations will see your righteousness, and all kings your glory. You will be called by a new name that the Lord's mouth will announce. ³ You will be a glorious crown in the Lord's hand, and a royal diadem in the palm of your God. ⁴ You will no longer be called Deserted, and your land will not be called Desolate; instead, you will be called My Delight is in Her, and your land Married; for the Lord delights in you, and your land will be married. ⁵ For as a young man marries a virgin, so your sons will marry you; and as a bridegroom rejoices over [his] bride, so your God will rejoice over you. ¹² And they will be called the Holy People, the Lord's Redeemed; and you will be called Cared For, A City Not Deserted.

ISAIAH 62:2-5,12

7. God cares so deeply for you that He wants to replace your losses and lavish unimaginable gifts on you. What gifts does Isaiah describe? Do you feel God's sheer delight in you—just you?

8. What could happen in your life if you live in your glory (2 Corinthians 4:17), experience God's delight and joy in you, and embrace your new name—your new identity in the larger story?

CONNECTING - 15 MINUTES

LEADER: *For those who have not yet pulled the first brick from their walls and discarded them, encourage them to take their bricks home and throw them in the garbage when they are ready to move ahead in their journey.*
This final "Connecting" time will focus on releasing burdens, pains, people, or questions to God through the helium balloon exercise.

LEADER INSTRUCTIONS FOR THE GROUP EXPERIENCE: *See page 122 too.*
Give each person in the group one helium-filled balloons and a fine-point marker for writing on the balloon. If it's dark outside, step 1 will have to be done inside or around some outside light source.

Say this to the group: "As huge as your loss is, it's not the end of your story. It doesn't define who you are or what God ultimately plans to do in and through you. Throughout our journey, we have discussed the importance of releasing our grasp on things we need to hand over to God.

Step 1: Think about the various burdens you might be carrying: guilt, shame, blame, disillusionment, discouragement, pain, false beliefs and vows, questions, or issues with specific people. Write those burdens on your balloon with a marker.

Step 2: In your own time ... when you are ready to make a conscious decision to release those burdens ... open up your hand to release your balloon and give your burdens to God. He's been waiting for you to allow Him to carry your burdens. Watch your balloon until you can no longer see it. This will remind you that you have released your burdens to God and they are no longer retrievable."

Step 3: Ask each group member while you are still outside ..."What would be the most helpful thing this group could do to support you as you continue to deal with your grief? How can we pray for you today?

MY PRAYER REQUESTS:

MY GROUP'S PRAYER REQUESTS:

In addition to specific prayer requests, thank God for the hope and healing that He has been progressively revealing to each individual and to the group. Thank Him for His extravagant love!

A QUESTION TO TAKE TO GOD:

✳ "God, how do You plan to redeem this season of pain and loss in my life?"

Redeeming the Tears Journal

REQUIRED SUPPLIES AND PREPARATION
FOR EACH SESSION

This section lists the supplies required for the Group Experiences in each session of the study. The procedural instructions for the experiences are also given within each session.

SESSION 1:
Supplies: - Menorah or a three-place candleholder
- Disposable lighter or large matches

Procedure:

Turn down the lights in the room, and use a menorah or a three-place candleholder to symbolize the presence of God. With the room dark or dim say, "Your life was going along normally when suddenly an event outside of your control struck and changed your life forever." Then, strike a match or ignite a disposal lighter. As you hold this small flame continue with, "In a moment, your life was dramatically changed. In that same moment though God—the Father, Son, and Holy Spirit—symbolized by this candle ... entered your life in a special way." Light the menorah or three candles. Feel free to briefly share about the darkness you experienced in your loss.

SESSION 2:
Supplies: - DVD player or Video cassette player
- Remote control
- Any movie to put in the player

Procedure:

Choose a movie to put in the DVD player or VCR that you set up before the session. Hit the Fast-Forward button and hand the remote control to one of your group members. Ask him or her to let it run a bit, and then randomly hit the Play button. Let the movie run for about 30 seconds and then stop it. Be sure people that have not seen this movie respond first. Then allow anyone who has seen it to fill in the blanks.

SESSION 3:
Supplies: - Bricks: At least one for each group member
- Large metal garbage can

Procedure:

Point out the bricks (one for each group member) you stacked up prior to this session. Ask your group members to close their eyes and imagine they are facing a brick wall. Explain that the wall represents those obstacles that stand in the way of moving beyond their pain and embracing life on the other side. Ask your group members to keep their eyes closed and ask God to reveal:

1. How tall and how broad is your wall?
2. When you face your wall, do you see an immovable mass, a long-term project, or a barrier easily removed?
3. Look around you. Is there anybody with you to help you tear down your wall?
4. Where is God in your picture? Next to you? Watching you struggle at a distance? On the other side of the wall? Nowhere in the picture?
5. How big is God in your picture?
6. In your picture, what does God want to do about your wall?
7. Are you ready at this point to take out the first brick from your wall? Everyone may not be ready and that's okay.

The first brick you remove from a wall is always the toughest one; the others fall more easily once the wall has been weakened. If you are truly ready to begin dismantling your wall, walk up one at a time, grab a brick, and discard it into the garbage can.

Don't feel pressured to take this step today. This step will not move you any closer to the other side of the wall unless it is authentic. If you need more time, it's really okay. The bricks will be here every week until you are ready.

SESSION 4:
Supplies: - Remaining bricks and the metal garbage can
         - Arrows or Darts: At least one for each group member
Procedure:
Again, continue to keep what remains of the stack of bricks and the metal garbage can from Session 3 available for your group members. If anyone is ready this week to remove the first brick from his or her wall, they may grab a brick, and toss it into the garbage can.

Direct the group's attention to the pile of arrows or darts (one for each member of the group) that you laid out prior to the session. Ask your group members to again close their eyes and imagine a battle scene. Ask your group members to keep their eyes closed and ask God to reveal:

1. What is the evil intent of the enemy for my life?
2. Where are his arrows embedded in my life as a result of past wounds? How old was I when these arrows were launched?
3. God, would you bring back specific memories and events where arrows were embedded in my lie?
4. What key messages (that is, lies) have been repeated each time the arrows fly?

Each person should take an arrow (or dart) from the pile as a needed reminder of the unseen battle and as an encouragement that as we draw near to God, we have access to powerful spiritual weapons when we are attacked again. What are specific ways that we can pray for you and support you this week?

Session 5:

Supplies: - Remaining bricks and the metal garbage can
Procedure:
Again, continue to keep what remains of the stack of bricks and the metal garbage can from Session 3 available for your group members. If anyone is ready this week to remove the first brick from his or her wall, they may grab a brick, and toss it into the garbage can.

The *Serenity Prayer*, written by Reinhold Niebuhr, depicts perfectly the attitude we should all be striving for at this point in our journey. Let's read it in unison as our prayer today.

God grant me the serenity
to accept the things I cannot change;
courage to change the things I can;
and wisdom to know the difference.
Living one day at a time;

Enjoying one moment at a time;
Accepting hardships as the pathway to peace;
Taking, as He did, this sinful world
as it is, not as I would have it;
Trusting that He will make all things right
if I surrender to His Will;
That I may be reasonably happy in this life
and supremely happy with Him
Forever.
Amen

Session 6:

Supplies: - Remaining bricks and the metal garbage can
       - Menorah or a three-place candleholder
       - Disposable lighter or large matches
Procedure:
Again, continue to keep what remains of the stack of bricks and the metal garbage can from Session 3 available for your group members. If anyone is ready this week to remove the first brick from his or her wall, they may grab a brick, and toss it into the garbage can.

Turn down the lights in the room, and relight the menorah or three-place candleholder from

Session 1 to symbolize the presence of God. With the room dark or dim, ask your group members to close their eyes. Say this: "As we have used the candles to represent the presence of God, close your eyes and envision God the Father, God the Son, and God the Holy Spirit walking into this room now. As they approach you, how do you feel? What is going through your mind?"

After a pause, say: "Many of us feel panicked or nervous, unsure whether we are good enough to be accepted. Or perhaps we even expect God to lash out at us for what we've done. But that's a lie from the lips of the enemy! The truth is that God created you in His image, and He not only loves you, but He truly enjoys you. The Father sent the Son to die in our place so we could regain our original glory. The Holy Spirit absolutely enjoys coming alongside to help you. In fact, as the awesome Trinity enters the room, what they really do is rush to your side, kneel down, and embrace you.

Pass out the candles you brought, one to each group member, and then read the steps and questions below:
1. Your candle represents your life, which God longs to rescue from "the domain of darkness" (Colossians 1:13), enabling you to walk in His light. Come forward one at a time, and recognize God is the source of light in our darkness. It is only as you encounter Him personally, and touch your candle to His light that truth ignites in your heart.
2. Once each person has lighted his or her candle, gather together in a circle. Notice that the intensity of the light increases as you draw closer together. That's the reality of Christian community.

SESSION 7:
Supplies: - Remaining bricks and the metal garbage can
Procedure:
Again, continue to keep what remains of the stack of bricks and the metal garbage can from Session 3 available for your group members. If anyone is ready this week to remove the first brick from his or her wall, they may grab a brick, and toss it into the garbage can.

In this "Connecting" time you'll allow time for everyone to share two simple memories from your group. Sharing fun times together enhances a group's connection. You may be amazed by the responses you hear from these simple questions.

BONUS SESSION:
Supplies: None
Procedure: See the session.
SESSION 8:

Supplies: - Remaining bricks
           - Helium-filled balloons on strings: At least one for each group member
           - Fine-point markers: At least one for each group member

Procedure:

For those who have not yet pulled the first brick from their walls and discarded them, encourage them to take their bricks home and throw them in the garbage when they are ready to move ahead in their journey.

This final "Connecting" time will focus on releasing burdens, pains, people, or questions to God through the helium balloon exercise.

Give each person in the group one helium-filled balloons and a fine-point marker for writing on the balloon. If it's dark outside, step 1 will have to be done inside or around some outside light source.

Say this to the group: "As huge as your loss is, it's not the end of your story. It doesn't define who you are or what God ultimately plans to do in and through you. Throughout our journey, we have discussed the importance of releasing our grasp on things we need to hand over to God.

Step 1: Think about the various burdens you might be carrying: guilt, shame, blame, disillusionment, discouragement, pain, false beliefs and vows, questions, or issues with specific people. Write those burdens on your balloon with a marker.

Step 2: In your own time ... when you are ready to make a conscious decision to release those burdens ... open up your hand to release your balloon and give your burdens to God. He has been waiting for you to allow Him to carry your burdens. Watch your balloon until you can no longer see it. This will remind you that you have released your burdens to God and they are no longer retrievable.

Step 3: Ask each group member while you are still outside ..."What would be the most helpful thing this group could do to support you as you continue to deal with your grief? How can we pray for you today?

Leading a Successful Grief and Loss Group

You will find a great deal of helpful information in this section that will be crucial for success as you lead your group.

Reading through this and utilizing the suggested principles and practices will greatly enhance the group experience. You need to accept the limitations of leadership. You cannot transform a life. You must lead your group to the Bible, the Holy Spirit, and the power of Christian community. By doing so your group will have all the tools necessary to walk through the grieving process and embrace life and hope on the other side. The grief process normally lasts longer than eight weeks. But the connections that are built and the truths learned with allow your group members to move toward wholeness.

Make the following things available at each session
- *Redeeming the Tears* book for each attendee
- Bible for each attendee
- Boxes of tissue
- Snacks and refreshments
- Dark chocolates
- Pens or pencils for each attendee

Most every session will demand other items be available. Check the list and make sure you have what is needed for each session.

The Setting

General Tips:
1. Prepare for each meeting by reviewing the material, praying for each group member, asking the Holy Spirit to join you at each meeting, and making Jesus the centerpiece of every experience.

2. Create the right environment by making sure chairs are arranged so each person can see the eyes of every other attendee. Set the room temperature at 69 degrees. Make sure pets are in a location where they cannot interrupt the meeting. Request that cell phones are turned off unless someone is expecting an emergency call. Have music playing as people arrive (volume low enough for people to converse) and, if possible, burn a sweet-smelling candle.

3. Try to have soft drinks and coffee available for early arrivals.

4. Have someone with the spiritual gift of hospitality ready to make any new attendees feel welcome.

5. Be sure there is adequate lighting so that everyone can read without straining.

6. There are four types of questions used in each session: Observation (What is the passage telling us?), Interpretation (What does the passage mean?), Self-revelation (How am I doing in light of the truth unveiled?), and Application (Now that I know what I know, what will I do to integrate this truth into my life?). You won't be able to use all the questions in each study, but be sure to use some from each of these types of questions.

7. Connect with group members away from group time. The amount of participation you have during your group meetings is directly related to the amount of time you connect with your group members away from the meeting time.

8. Don't get impatient about the depth of relationship group members are experiencing. Building real Christian Community takes time.

9. Be sure pens and/or pencils are available for attendees at each meeting.

10. Never ask someone to pray aloud without first getting their permission.

Every Meeting:

1. Before the icebreakers, do not say, "Now we're going to do an icebreaker." The meeting should feel like a conversation from beginning to end, not a classroom experience.

2. Be certain every member responds to the icebreaker questions. The goal is for every person to hear his or her own voice early in the meeting. People will then feel comfortable to converse later on. If members can't think of a response, let them know you'll come back to them after the others have spoken.

3. Remember, a great group leader talks less than 10% of the time. If you ask a question and no one answers, just wait. If you create an environment where you fill the gaps of silence, the group will quickly learn they needn't join you in the conversation.

4. Don't be hesitant to call people by name as you ask them to respond to questions or to give their opinions. Be sensitive, but engage everyone in the conversation.

5. Don't ask people to read aloud unless you have gotten their permission prior to the meeting. Feel free to ask for volunteers to read.

The Group

Each small group has it's own persona. Every group is made up of a unique set of personalities, backgrounds, and life experiences. This diversity creates a dynamic distinctive to that specific group of people. Embracing the unique character of your group and the individual's in that group is vital to group members experiencing all you're hoping for.

Treat each person as special, responsible, and valuable members of this Christian community. By doing so you'll bring out the best in each of them thus creating a living, breathing, life-changing group dynamic.

What Can You Expect?

Because group members are still experiencing numbness and emotions are stirring within them, at the outset, members will be on their best behavior. Most attendees will, as they understand the openness necessary and requested by the group, withdraw for at time.

Some attendees will experience fatigue which will lead to them shutting down emotionally. This is natural and is one of the things our body does to prevent emotional overload.

There are some emotions and phases unique to people dealing with grief. You need to be aware of these.

Anger – normal, but maybe difficult to express due to shame or guilt. Clearly directed in the case of a divorce or job loss. Can be turned inward (depression).

Guilt – Sometimes called the "What ifs" or the "If onlys".

Sadness – This is generally in direct proportion to the attachment to the person or object lost. The greater the loss, the deeper the sadness.

Anxiety and Helplessness - Fear of the unknown can increase anxiety.

Frustration – Adjusting to the absence of things needed and cherished is normal. Becomes a problem when there are demands to go back to the way it was

Depression – When the anger of a loss is directed inward

Loss of Identity – That which was lost is what gives some persons their sense of identity. Their self-worth is built around the job they use to have, the spouse they use to love and care for. When that thing no longer exists in their lives they find themselves without and are lost in a sea of unknown meaning.

You will be the most helpful when you focus on how the each individual is adjusting and reminding them that these emotions are normal. When short tempers, changes in physical habits, such as sleep, eating, apathy, and others appear to be long term, refer them to a pastor or competent Christian counselor. You can get a list of counselors from your pastor and other ministers.

Holidays and special occasions are especially difficult for people who are in the grief process. What was once a happy time is now brings difficulty and pain.

Places may also bring back memories that are difficult to deal with alone. If a member has an engagement in a location that would be a painful reminder of the past go with them and/or ask the group if one of them might be there for this individual. You may hear, "This is something I have to do alone." You can respect their desire to be strong, but remind them that even alone, it is God who will give them strength, and that you will pray for them.

WHAT CAN YOU DO?

Support – Provide plenty of time for support among the group members. Encourage members to connect with each other between meetings when necessary. Some examples are:
a) arranging a funeral
b) coping with the side effects of treatment,
c) how to look for a job
d) how to apply for financial assistance
e) mowing the grass
f) cleaning someone's home

Shared Feelings – Reassure the members how normal their feelings are; even if relief and sadness are mixed together. Encourage the members to share their feelings with one another.

Advice Giving – Avoid giving advice. Encourage cross-talk (members talking to each other), but limit advice giving. Should and ought to statements tend to increase the guilt the loss has already created.

Silence – Silence is not a problem. Even though it may seem awkward, silence is just a sign that people are not ready to talk. It DOES NOT mean they aren't thinking or feeling. If the silence needs to be broken, be sure you break it with the desire to move forward.

Prayer — Prayer is vital to healing. Starting and ending with prayer is important. However, people may need prayer in the middle of the session. Here's a way to know when the time is right to pray. If a member is sharing and you sense a need to pray, then begin to look for a place to add it.

Feelings vs. Right Choices and Thinking — There may be a temptation to overemphasize feelings rather that choices and thinking. It is important that you keep the focus on moving forward regardless of how we feel. Our feelings may make the journey slow, but left to feelings only, progress will shut down.

As you move toward the end of the study, be aware that it is a bittersweet time for the group. It will be painful for them to say goodbye to one another. Set a time for the group to have a reunion.

Acknowledgments

This project was a true team effort. We wish to thank the team that labored to make this life-changing small-group experience a reality.

Writers and key contributors: Dr. Paul Hardy (P.L.A.C.E. concept), Ron Keck (Critical Path to Healing construct), Ben Colter, Rick Howerton, and Ransom Bennett.

Editorial team: Sarah Hogg and Melissa Colter

Art direction and interior design: Scott Lee

Cover design: Roy Roper of Anderson Thomas Design

How Ya' Doin' Really?

1	2	3	4	5	6	7	8	9	10

I can't believe this has happened

I feel stuck in my pain and sorrow like I'll never recover

I'm learning to grieve and I view it as a journey

I'm making progress on the journey

I'm connected with God and hopeful about the future

	DATE	RATING
Week 1	_____	_____
Week 2	_____	_____
Week 3	_____	_____
Week 4	_____	_____
Week 5	_____	_____
Week 6	_____	_____
Week 7	_____	_____
Week 8	_____	_____